HEALTH AND SAFETY GAMES FOR TRAINERS

Health and Safety Games for Trainers

Graham Roberts-Phelps

Gower

© Graham Roberts-Phelps 1999

The materials that appear in this book, other than those quoted from prior sources, may be reproduced for education/training activities. There is no requirement to obtain special permission for such uses.

This permission statement is limited to reproduction of materials for educational or training events. Systematic or large-scale reproduction or distribution – or inclusion of items in publication for sale – may be carried out only with prior written permission from the publisher.

First published 1997 as *Quizzes and Icebreakers for Safety Trainers* by 80/20 Training Limited.

This edition published by
Gower Publishing Limited
Gower House
Croft Road
Aldershot
Hampshire GU11 3HR
England

Gower
Old Post Road
Brookfield
Vermont 05036
USA

Graham Roberts-Phelps has asserted his right under the Copyright, Designs and Patents Act 1988 to be identified as the author of this work.

British Library Cataloguing in Publication Data
Roberts-Phelps, Graham
  Health and safety games for trainers
  1. Industrial safety–Management 2. Industrial safety–
  Problems, exercises, etc. 3. Safety education, Industrial
  4. Employees–Training of
  I. Title
  363.1'1'068

ISBN 0 566 08202 0 Hardback
ISBN 0 566 08203 9 Looseleaf

Library of Congress Cataloging-in-Publication Data
Roberts-Phelps, Graham
  Health and safety games for trainers / Graham Roberts-Phelps
    p. cm.
    ISBN 0-566-08202-0. —ISBN 0–566–08203–9 (loose-leaf)
    1. Safety education, Industrial. I. Title.
  T55.2.R63 1999
  658.3'82—dc21   98–53696
                                                                                    CIP

Typeset in Times by Bournemouth Colour Press, Parkstone and printed in Great Britain at the University Press, Cambridge.

Contents

1. Introduction

Overview

About this Book

How to Use this Book

The Main Formats of Games and Activities

Five Ways to Get the Best Out of This Book

Safety Case Studies

Learning Log
  Trainer's notes
  Handout

Overview

Health and Safety Games for Trainers is a collection of energizing, ice-breaking, brain-teasing, thought-provoking ideas designed to make your training course more effective, interactive and involving.

Designed and collated by Graham Roberts-Phelps, it has been thoroughly tried and tested in a number of different environments.

If you have any suggestions for inclusion in a future volume, or have any questions regarding these quizzes/activities please contact 80/20 Training Ltd, tel: (44) 01908 587462.

About this Book

These safety training games and activities have been created and used extensively in the training of safety skills. Relevant to all types of industry and successful with personnel of any age, experience and background, they are designed with the following characteristics in mind.

EASY TO RUN

Simple to follow, step-by-step instructions mean that a minimum of preparation and experience is required. The time saved can then be devoted to either enhancing the basic activity or creating company-specific material.

COMPLETE

Each activity comes with everything necessary – handouts, worksheets and trainer's notes.

GENERIC

Whether you are a manufacturer or a service provider, private or public sector, industrial or retail, the activities and exercises are focused on generic safety knowledge and skills – skills that are completely transferable across all organizations and situations. Most use an 'open content' approach, which means that delegates use their own examples and experiences as the main subject, making the exercises automatically and completely relevant. (They are, of course, easy to customize should you wish to do so.)

VARIED

The activities range from 15-minute ice-breakers to 90-minute role plays, and include quizzes, games, questionnaires, problem-solving activities and discussions. This means that the training can be kept varied and interesting, and topics approached from several different angles.

OPEN CONTENT

As the 'content' of many of the activities is provided by the delegates themselves, the material is instantly relevant and appropriate.

How to Use this Book

Each type of game or activity is detailed in a clear set of instructions for the trainer, with information contained under the following headings.

OUTLINE

A brief outline of each exercise is contained in a simple box. This shows the format of the activity (pairs, groups, etc.), the type of the exercise (e.g. discussion) and the resources needed (in most cases a standard flip chart and overhead projector (OHP) are all that are required). Estimated times for various parts of the exercise are also given.

OBJECTIVE

This section gives a short summary of the aims of the activity. In many, it is recommended that you share this objective with the group as it will help them to focus when completing the activity.

PROCEDURE

This section details the training instructions and explains how to introduce, run and conclude each activity. These instructions are kept deliberately brief. This is of great benefit when referring to the notes whilst running the course, as the information you need can be easily found, read and relayed to the group.

Instructions have been phrased in a general way, and, where possible, avoid giving the actual words to be used. Very few trainers would use them *verbatim* and might find it condescending.

HANDOUTS

These follow the trainer's notes, contain brief instructions to the delegates on how to perform the task or activity, and are often given in a structured format or as a worksheet. The benefit of using the handouts provided is that the communication is often much clearer, and it gives delegates a reference during the exercise. Answers to the handouts are provided in the Answers section (pp. 203–226).

The Main Formats of Games and Activities

INDIVIDUAL WORKING

When delegates are required to work on their own, perhaps completing a questionnaire or worksheet, it allows a degree of self-reflection and is an excellent contrast to the role play and group work. Many people are happy working in this way, indeed it follows the pattern of learning established at school.

PAIRS

Based on the principle that 'two heads are better that one', this format asks delegates to work in pairs, working through a problem, questionnaire or worksheet jointly.

It is useful to pair people carefully, balancing personalities and experience. Make sure that both are contributing and making notes. On longer courses, it is a good idea to change these pairs occasionally. If the numbers are odd, one group can be stretched to three.

SMALL GROUPS

Small groups of between three and eight people are most suitable for working on a problem, issue or discussion, as well as in free-format ideas sessions.

The size of your main group will of course determine how small you can divide the groups, but from general observation it is difficult to circulate or monitor more than about four groups.

MAIN GROUP

The whole group (of approximately eight or more people) might run a general discussion or activity.

Five Ways to Get the Best Out of this Book

1. USE THE EXERCISES WITH CONFIDENCE

All the activities and exercises in this book have been developed and used in professional training courses and seminars, and are all proven to be effective on a range of different types of courses and delegates.

2. BE FLEXIBLE

Because of the 'open content' style, they are suitable for most types of organizations and training courses. This approach also makes them easy to adapt to your needs. You might want to experiment and develop your own variations of these games and activities, for example by adding in new elements or lengthening particular segments. You will also find that because of the 'open-content' nature of the activities that they will vary slightly in execution, with different groups having different reactions and results.

3. STRUCTURE YOUR TRAINING

By mixing at least three different formats (working in small groups/pairs, as individuals and in the group as a whole) to cover the same points, you can greatly increase learning retention and effectiveness. People will have different preferences and gain more from a variety of formats during a course.

4. MAKE NOTES AND ADAPT

Customise or edit these exercises to better suit your own style of training as you gain experience in running them. Make notes in the margin whilst preparing the course or during it in order to remember the points for next time.

5. TRAIN, DON'T TALK

Most of the trainer's time is spent not telling people what to do, instead it is trying to get them to **do** what they already **know**.

These games and activities are designed to help people learn. If you find yourself talking rather less than you might do normally, don't worry about it!

Safety Case Studies

You might find these useful when discussing safety issues.

1. In one Midlands factory, excess material from a component casting process was removed using a large pedestal grinder. The operator had to hold each component firmly and then push it against the grinder and its support. Vibration to the hands was extremely hazardous, mainly because the support was poorly built. A new support was constructed, which brought the amount of vibration well within acceptable levels.

2. By reviewing their use of chemicals, a fish processing company helped safeguard its workers' health and made cost savings at the same time. Following the Control of Substances Hazardous to Health (COSHH) Regulations 1988, they stopped using chemicals that weren't essential to the processing, and found less hazardous alternatives to replace others. They not only reduced the risk of ill health, but also saved money and storage space by using a smaller range of chemicals.

3. A company with loud machines wanted to reduce noise levels to below 90 dB(A) as required by the Noise at Work Regulations 1989. The workforce played a major part in the design and development of noise enclosures which were fitted around noisy machines. The noise levels were checked to see if the target had been reached – it had. The workforce felt that the management had demonstrated it was serious about improving working conditions.

4. Operators assembling transmission housings for helicopters used a ratchet spanner to screw in steel pegs. Several operators reported elbow and upper arm pain. The task involved a lot of forceful, awkward and repetitive movements, which could have led to serious upper limb disorders.

The company introduced pneumatic nut runners. These screwed in the pegs with a simple squeeze of the trigger. As well as reducing the number of reports of pain and stopping the problems worsening, the company found the unit assembly time nearly halved, and the product quality improved.

5. A company installed ventilation equipment to control the dust made when weighing powdered chemicals. To make sure the equipment was effectively reducing dust levels, the airflow rates of the ventilation equipment and airborne levels of the chemicals handled were measured routinely. A fall in air flow rates or high levels of dust triggered an investigation to find out why the control equipment was not working properly.

6. MacFish Ltd, Fraserburgh, Scotland, has grown with regard to health and safety since it became involved in the Health and Safety Executive's 'Lighten the Load' campaign in 1994. It has invested in plant and equipment which has helped to reduce the manual handling of products at various stages of production. The workforce has been made aware of issues which affect them and they have been helpful in raising and implementing safety initiatives. The growth has been testing at times and success has been achieved on numerous occasions.

MacFish Ltd was proud to participate in the 'Lighten the Load' campaign and is looking forward to improving health and safety in the workplace. The company will be involved in future campaigns.

7. Northampton General Hospital Trust has been involved in the 'Health at Work in the NHS' campaign – a health promotion programme to encourage healthier lifestyles and safer conditions for patients and NHS staff. Core elements focused on health and safety issues, and policies and risk management strategies, leading to the Trust gaining two awards in the Health Promoting Trust Awards Scheme in 1995.

These successes have only been possible with the backing and commitment of top management, the acceptance of line management health and safety responsibilities and cooperation of all 3 000 members of hospital staff.

A new Health and Safety Action Plan has been published. This will finalize the purchase of manual handling equipment, such as patient hoists, and promote and implement a new fire training programme for all staff.

8. The Cheese Company, Appleby Creamery, Cumbria, is committed to risk reduction and supports the Health and Safety Executive's 'Good Health Is Good Business' campaign. Its positive attitude towards tackling occupational health across the company has helped to reduce accidents by 40 per cent over the last three years against an increase in productivity of 25 per cent.

A comprehensive programme of 900 risk assessments were carried out across ten sites. These identified the key areas in which time and money had to be invested to achieve a reduction in accidents and improve efficiency.

A broad range of projects followed, including the installation of mechanical lifting assistance through the use of vacuum lifting heads at the Taw Valley Creamery in Devon and Oswestry packing facility in Shropshire. In both places, 20kg cheese blocks are transferred from pallets to conveyers. End-of-line scissors lifts and adjustable pallet trucks are being installed at the Appleby Creamery in Cumbria. At the Cheshire site, Reeces of Malpas, projects are underway to upgrade cheese milling and pressing operations, reducing pulling and handling.

9. A council surveyed its buildings to check for the presence of asbestos and to assess its condition. As a result of the survey, the council now keeps a central record of the location of all asbestos materials. All repair and maintenance work is also coordinated centrally, and workers are informed if the material they are working on contains asbestos. As an additional safeguard, all asbestos materials are labelled. The council, therefore, has a system in place to prevent workers from unknowingly working on asbestos materials.

10. A company moulding plastic components, using compressed air guns to clear powder deposits, measured noise levels of 105 dB(A) near to where employees were working. By replacing the air guns' nozzles, at £40 each, with ones reducing the turbulence within the tube, noise levels were reduced by up to 10 dB(A). The new tools were also stronger.

11. In the car industry, one company found that the noise generated during the machining of alternator end-castings was 104 dB(A). The solution was to apply, at a cost of £40, a simple damping treatment to reduce the amount of vibration. As a result, noise levels decreased by 16 dB(A). In addition, the quality of the cut improved and machining time was reduced.

12. Operators in a manufacturing plant manoeuvred a drum of steel wire weighing 365 kg into a machine for winding springs. There were reports of back and shoulder pain and one serious back injury. For just £20, the company made a long handle to attach to the drum making it much easier to move. The operators were happier using the handle and there have been no injuries or reports of pain since.

13. A worker assembling 50 manifolds per hour using a manual screwdriver began to suffer discomfort in both hands. Diagnosed as having tenosynovitis in one hand and carpal tunnel syndrome in the other, she was off work for four months. In order to stop this happening again, a rig was fitted to hold the manifolds and a torque-controlled air screwdriver was introduced. This cost only £500. The risk of injury has been greatly reduced, there is less material wastage and product quality has improved.

14. Two workers from an electroplating factory had symptoms suggestive of occupational asthma. Diagnosis was confirmed by lung-function tests in the workplace, but no causative agent was apparent on initial enquiries. Then a worker produced a safety data sheet describing a lacquer containing 7 per cent isophorone diisocyanate. The Health and Safety Executive (HSE) then visited the factory and confirmed that isocyanates were being used and the employer was exceeding the maximum exposure limit. On the HSE's advice the employer installed extraction equipment which has dramatically reduced the levels of isocyanates in the working environment. However, the two workers who had become sensitized were no longer able to carry on working in the factory, as their symptoms recurred upon exposure to isocyanates. The first worker took early retirement on medical grounds and has received compensation for occupational asthma, whereas the second worker has changed employment and has applied for compensation.

Learning Log

Trainer's notes

> **Outline**
> **Format:**   *Individuals*
> **Type:**   *Assessment activity*
> **Time:**   *N/A*
> **Resources:** *Handout provided*

Objective

To gather information throughout the course.

Procedure

Give the delegates the handout provided at the beginning of the course. Tell them to log the ideas and key points they hear during the course which they may want to follow up in their workplace.

At the end of the session, you could gather their key points and discuss.

📄 Learning Log

Name	Date

During the training session there will be many useful ideas and learning points that you will want to apply in the workplace. Please note them as you go through on this form.

KEY IDEA OR LEARNING POINT	HOW I WILL APPLY THESE

Reproduced from *Health and Safety Games for Trainers*, Graham Roberts-Phelps, Gower, Aldershot

2. True/False Quizzes

Quizzes 1–9

Trainer's notes

Outline	
Format:	*Small groups*
Type:	*An energizer*
Time:	*5 minutes, plus discussion*
Resources:	*Handouts provided*

Objective

This is a learning activity and a good course 'energizer'. By keeping the session slightly competitive, and occasionally light-hearted, delegates will learn and have fun.

Procedure

Start by running a short discussion amongst delegates. Explain that this activity is similar to a quiz show, except that the prizes aren't so grand!

Divide delegates into small groups, if possible balancing experience and knowledge.

Distribute the handouts and ask trainees to work through the statements, marking each as either true or false.

Discuss any questions and issues that may arise.

📄 Quiz 1: Safety Awareness

Consider each of the following statements carefully and mark each with a ✓ as either true or false.

Statement	True	False
1. Every accident or injury can be prevented or avoided.		
2. Every accident, or work-related injury or discomfort is caused in some way by human error.		
3. You cannot motivate people to be safer, only to enforce rules and penalties.		
4. Left to their own devices, people and organizations will take unnecessary risks and cut corners.		
5. Safety regulations and legislation create very real obligations not only for companies and organizations, but also for their directors, managers and the individual employees.		
6. In safety law, ignorance (i.e. not knowing the safety law) is a defence.		
7. If there is an accident, health and safety law is interpreted so that the company or the organization has to *prove* that it was not at fault.		
8. The Health and Safety at Work Act 1974 is the main law that covers everyone at work and all work premises, except visitors and sub-contractors.		
9. Individuals have to ensure their health and safety and that of others around them who could be affected by what they do or fail to do.		
10. In some cases, safety inspectors will allow some variances to safety standards if an organization cannot afford specialist equipment.		

    Reproduced from *Health and Safety Games for Trainers*, Graham Roberts-Phelps, Gower, Aldershot

📄 Quiz 2: Safety Awareness

Consider each of the following statements carefully and mark each with a ✓ as either true or false.

Statement	True	False
1. Safety studies have highlighted that small firms (fewer than 50 employees) have worse accident records than large organizations.		
2. Many small companies make matters worse by not reporting most accidents.		
3. Employers must take every practical step to remove hazards and reduce or eliminate risks, so long as this is cost-effective.		
4. The law interprets this as taking every possible precaution, and cost is not considered as an excuse for failure to do this.		
5. All organizations employing five or more people must have a written and up-to-date health and safety policy.		
6. Written risk assessments must be carried out regularly by companies as part of the implementation of their safety policy.		
7. All staff must be fully trained and informed of the company's safety policy and procedures, and given the skills and knowledge necessary to carry out their normal work duties.		
8. All employees must take reasonable care to protect themselves and their colleagues. Failure to do so is in breach of the HASAW Act.		
9. Health and Safety Executive inspectors can visit without notice and have right of entry. They have the power to stop work, close premises and even prosecute.		
10. Accidents do not happen by themselves, they are often caused by ordinary people not taking safety seriously.		

Reproduced from *Health and Safety Games for Trainers*, Graham Roberts-Phelps, Gower, Aldershot

📄 Quiz 3: Display Screen Equipment

Consider each of the following statements carefully and mark each with a ✓ as either true or false.

Statement	True	False
1. VDU Safety regulations have been introduced to meet the needs of the high-volume or intensive users of computers and VDU terminals.		
2. All VDU or computer work stations must be assessed regularly, for example once a year, and a record kept of those assessments.		
3. Regular improvements to equipment or working practices recommended in a written assessment, must be fully implemented under the guidelines within the Health and Safety regulations.		
4. All members of staff classified as habitual users of VDU or display screen equipment must be trained in safe working practices.		
5. Work routines must be organized so there are routine breaks or changes of activity.		
6. Undue stress may be manifested in the form of headaches, backaches or general fatigue.		
7. All work stations, that is the computer or VDU equipment, together with associated peripherals such as printers, desks and chairs, must be assessed to check whether they meet the required standards.		
8. Unless the equipment has been manufactured and supplied in the last three to four years or since 1994 or 1995, it is unlikely that it will actually meet these new regulations.		
9. The hazards that may exist from using VDUs are eye strain, headaches, back or upper limb problems.		
10. VDUs and computers cause undue emotional stress.		

Reproduced from *Health and Safety Games for Trainers*, Graham Roberts-Phelps, Gower, Aldershot

📄 Quiz 4: Risk Assessment

Consider each of the following statements carefully and mark each with a ✓ as either true or false.

Statement	True	False
1. Every accident or injury can be reduced, prevented or avoided.		
2. Large firms (more than 100 employees) have a worse record of safety than smaller firms.		
3. Risk assessments are most important where large numbers of people might be affected.		
4. It is a legal requirement to complete a risk assessment for all employees.		
5. It is a legal requirement to complete an assessment only for those working with significant hazards or in higher risk areas.		
6. When following up recommendations, cost can be an excuse for not implementing certain measures.		
7. Risk assessments should be completed exactly four times a year.		
8. There are many penalties for companies and individuals that fail in their duty to carry out suitable risk assessments.		
9. Ten million working days are lost each year due to health and safety related accidents, sickness or injury.		
10. Small firms (fewer than 50 employees) have a worse safety record than larger firms.		

📄 Quiz 5: Safety for Managers

Consider each of the following statements carefully and mark each with a ✓ as either true or false.

Statement	True	False
1. Every accident or injury can be prevented or avoided by spending money on safety resources.		
2. Every accident or work-related injury or discomfort is caused in some way by human error.		
3. You cannot motivate people to be safer, only to enforce rules and penalties.		
4. Left to their own devices, people and organizations will take unnecessary risks and cut corners.		
5. Over 400 people are killed at work every year.		
6. Back injuries are the most common form of work-related injury.		
7. Managers and directors can be fired and even jailed for failure to enforce safety measures.		
8. Of the three essentials that must be provided for in the workplace, your computer is the most important!		
9. HSE safety inspectors have the right of entry and the right to interview and take samples only with an organization's permission.		
10. Safety inspections should be carried out exactly four times a year.		

Reproduced from *Health and Safety Games for Trainers*, Graham Roberts-Phelps, Gower, Aldershot

📄 Quiz 6: Environmental Awareness

Consider each of the following statements carefully and mark each with a ✓ as either true or false.

Statement	True	False
1. The largest domestic consumer of water is the toilet.		
2. Annually in the UK 450 million animals are killed for food.		
3. The average milk bottle is used 53 times.		
4. Every three months, the United States throws away enough aluminium to rebuild its entire commercial airfleet.		
5. It is estimated that a 1 per cent reduction in ozone could result in 15 000 new cases of skin cancer in the United States alone.		
6. Every year, there are 3.5 million medical tests administered on animals.		
7. Britons spend about £30 million per year on garden pesticides.		
8. Around 25 pints (14 litres) of tree-killing solvent are emitted into the atmosphere when a single car is painted.		
9. If everyone in Britain placed one day's rubbish in Trafalgar Square, the pile would reach up to Nelson's feet.		
10. It takes half a gallon (2 litres) of water to boil a pan full of pasta and a gallon (4 litres) to wash the pan.		

📄 Quiz 7: Safe Manual Handling

Consider each of the following statements carefully and mark each with a ✓ as either true or false.

Statement	True	False
1. On any one working day, there are over 90 000 people off work with back problems.		
2. All employees must be aware of the common hazards that exist with the manual movement of loads and frequent forced or awkward movements of the body.		
3. Employees should be trained on how to lift safely, as well as how to use any lifting or manual handling equipment or facilities provided. These include hoists, trolleys, trucks and steps.		
4. Manual handling must be eliminated wherever possible. The Manual Handling Regulations state that you must avoid manual handling if a safer way, e.g. mechanical, is practical.		
5. Employees should not be asked to lift heavy or awkward objects, either without training or if the goods are above the safe weight limits and, therefore, represent an unreasonable level of risk of injury.		
6. Protective equipment may also be needed to protect hands and feet when lifting.		
7. It is estimated that over 5.5 million working days are lost in Britain every year directly as a result of back-related, or manual handling related injuries or disorders.		
8. Research by the Health and Safety Executive shows that over 30 per cent of all injuries in the workplace are due or related to lifting, handling or load carrying of some form.		
9. It is only those people who carry heavy weights or have to lift frequently in their job, who are at risk.		
10. All manual handling accidents are back-related.		

Reproduced from *Health and Safety Games for Trainers*, Graham Roberts-Phelps, Gower, Aldershot

📄 Quiz 8: Fire Safety

Consider each of the following statements carefully and mark each with a ✓ as either true or false.

Statement	True	False
1. A safety sign with a blue background and white writing signifies a mandatory instruction.		
2. A safety sign with a green background and white writing signifies fire escapes and first aid boxes.		
3. When hearing the fire alarm, you should leave the building quickly and calmly.		
4. When you see a sign with a diamond shape and either red, blue, yellow, white or green background and black writing, you should not touch it without taking special care.		
5. Over two million accidents occur at work every year.		
6. Fire extinguishers should have a statutory test every 12 months and the cylinder should be replaced at least every five years.		
7. All fire extinguishers are red. The writing/band around the cylinder will indicate the contents.		
8. A black band indicates CO_2.		
9. A green band indicates Halon, a blue band BCF, and a red band water.		
10. Records of fire alarm testing and maintenance are not always necessary.		

📄 Quiz 9: COSHH Safety

Consider each of the following statements carefully and mark each with a ✓ as either true or false.

Statement	True	False
1. We must all consider using first 'safety' a first when using hazardous substances.		
2. Protective clothing is not always necessary when using hazardous substances.		
3. It is not always necessary to read instructions and data sheets, if you think you know the information.		
4. Always work closely with others when carrying out risk assessments.		
5. When storing and labelling hazardous substances, great care should be taken.		
6. It is necessary to inform workers if they are likely to come into contact with hazardous substances.		
7. No special training is required in the use of hazardous substances.		
8. Antidotes or neutralizing agents should always be available and clearly marked close to hazardous substances.		
9. It is necessary for COSHH data sheets to be available on all hazardous material.		
10. It is the manufacturer's responsibility, not the user's, to provide clear labels, signs and warnings.		

Reproduced from *Health and Safety Games for Trainers*, Graham Roberts-Phelps, Gower, Aldershot

3. Knowledge Tests

Tests 1–10

Trainer's notes

Outline	
Format:	*Small groups/pairs*
Type:	*Quiz-based energizer*
Time:	*15 minutes, plus discussion*
Resources:	*Handouts provided, flip chart*

Objective

The purpose of this exercise is to test the delegates' knowledge of safety, and in particular the points that you may have covered in previous discussions, presentations or training videos. By keeping the session slightly competitive, and occasionally light-hearted, delegates will learn and have fun.

Procedure

Distribute the handouts and ask the groups to work through the questions, discussing each within the group. There should be unanimous agreement for each question.

After each handout keep the score on a flip chart and continue until all the handouts are used up. You may choose to award part-points for nearly right answers. Alternatively, allow each team to answer a set number of questions of their choice, for example five or six. Discuss any questions and issues that may arise.

Run this exercise in a lively and up-tempo manner, allowing the delegates a chance to enjoy both the spirit of friendly competition and any humour that may arise.

📄 Test 1: Safety Awareness

Working in pairs or small groups, discuss and answer the following questions.

Question	Answer
1. List three things that employers are legally bound to do.	1. 2. 3.
2. List three things that employees are legally bound to do.	1. 2. 3.
3. List three pieces of recent EC legislation that may affect you.	1. 2. 3.
4. List three essentials that must be provided for in the workplace.	1. 2. 3.
5. List three hazards with potential to cause harm in the workplace.	1. 2. 3.
6. List three common causes of accidents in the workplace.	1. 2. 3.
7. What is the difference between a hazard and a risk?	
8. Small firms (fewer than 50 employees) have a worse safety record than larger firms.	True or False?
9. How many accidents occur at work every year?	(a) 600 000 (b) 1 600 000 (c) 2 200 000

Reproduced from *Health and Safety Games for Trainers*, Graham Roberts-Phelps, Gower, Aldershot

📄 Test 2: Safety at Work

Working in pairs or small groups, discuss and answer the following questions.

Question	Answer
1. How many working days are lost each year due to health and safety related accidents, sickness or injury?	(a) 10 million (b) 20 million (c) 30 million
2. What is the most common form of accident/injury in the workplace?	
3. How many people are killed at work every year?	(a) 200 (b) 600 (c) 800
4. List three negative attitudes that contribute towards accidents.	1. 2. 3.
5. List three positive attitudes that prevent accidents, illness and injury.	1. 2. 3.
6. How many people suffer ill-health, either caused or made worse by work conditions?	1. 600 000 2. 1 600 000 3. 2 200 000
7. The workplace temperature must be kept at a reasonable level – what should this be?	(a) 14°C (b) 16°C (c) 22°C
8. Are staff and safety representatives involved in health and safety consultations?	Yes or no?
9. List three common tasks which can cause back injury.	1. 2. 3.
10. How can the above tasks be prevented to reduce the risk?	1. 2. 3.

📄 Test 3: Fire Safety

Working in pairs or small groups, discuss and answer the following questions.

Question	Answer
1. What three actions should you take if you discover a fire?	1. 2. 3.
2. What is the most important information you must provide when you call the fire brigade?	
3. Name the four types of fire extinguisher and the colours of their bands.	1. 2. 3. 4.
4. Describe in three simple steps how you would operate a fire extinguisher.	1. 2. 3.
5. When a fire breaks out, which is the biggest killer?	(a) Panic (b) Flames (c) Smoke
6. List three things that you can do to prevent smoke spreading through the building in the event of a fire.	1. 2. 3.
7. What should you do first before you fight any electrical fire?	
8. In order for a fire to survive, three things must be present – what are they?	1. 2. 3.
9. In your place of work, what do you consider the **five** greatest potential fire hazards.	1. 2. 3. 4. 5.
10. What should you do if you discover a liquid petroleum gas leak?	(a) Leave it until it is empty (b) Turn off the valve and move the cylinder outside (c) Locate the leak with a match (d) Locate the leak with soapy water

     Reproduced from *Health and Safety Games for Trainers*, Graham Roberts-Phelps, Gower, Aldershot

📄 Test 4: Manual Handling

Working in pairs or small groups, discuss and answer the following questions.

Question	Answer
1. How many working days are lost every year due to manual handling related accidents, injuries or disorders?	(a) 5.5 million (b) 3 million (c) 1 million
2. Name three high-risk manual handling activities.	1. 2. 3.
3. What are the six steps for the prevention of back injuries and manual handling disorders?	1. 2. 3. 4. 5. 6.
4. What is the name of the regulations which govern the lifting, loading or carrying of objects?	
5. What is the manual handling safety weight guideline for lifting an item from the floor to knee or waist level?	
6. List some things to consider before attempting to lift an object or perform a series of repetitive lifting tasks.	
7. List some possible injuries that might be caused by incorrect or improper lifting.	
8. List some things to consider when lifting heavy objects.	
9. What percentage of reported manual handling accidents are caused by manual handling or lifting?	
10. On average, how long does an injury result in the person being off work?	(a) ten days (b) 20 days (c) 30 days

📄 Test 5: COSHH

Working in pairs or small groups, discuss and answer the following questions.

Question	Answer
1. What does COSHH stand for?	
2. Give your definition of 'substances hazardous to health'.	
3. List three examples of hazardous substances from your workplace or environment that are covered by the COSHH Regulations.	1. 2. 3.
4. List three examples of hazardous substances that might be found in your own home.	1. 2. 3.
5. List two substances that are **not** covered by the COSHH Regulations.	1. 2.
6. What three things must someone know about before being able to carry out a COSHH assessment?	1. 2. 3.
7. List three things that employees **must** be trained in before working with hazardous substances.	1. 2. 3.
8. What does CHIP stand for?	
9. List three examples of good practice when working with hazardous substances.	1. 2. 3.
10. Give an example of circumstances under which exposure monitoring and health surveillance would be required.	

   Reproduced from *Health and Safety Games for Trainers*, Graham Roberts-Phelps, Gower, Aldershot

📄 Test 6: Display Screen Equipment

Working in pairs or small groups, discuss and answer the following questions.

Question	Answer
1. List five key considerations of safe working with display screen equipment.	1. 2. 3. 4. 5.
2. Name three possible symptoms commonly associated with working with display screen equipment.	1. 2. 3.
3. Name any three individual items to consider when assessing a work station for VDU safety.	1. 2. 3.
4. Who is responsible for making sure that you are working safely when using computer or visual display equipment?	(a) You (b) Your manager or supervisor (c) The company (d) The computer manufacturer (e) All of the above
5. How often should work stations be assessed?	
6. Who should carry out this assessment?	
7. When using a keyboard, what position should your elbows be in?	(a) Slightly above the level of the desk (b) Level (c) Wherever is most comfortable
8. What is the best distance to sit away from the screen?	(a) 12 inches (b) 18 inches (c) 24 inches
9. VDUs or computer screens should **not** be used by pregnant women because of the danger of radiation.	True or False

📄 Test 7: Display Screen Equipment

Working in pairs or small groups, write a definition against each of the following computer or VDU words/terms.

	Term	Definition
1.	Display screen	
2.	VDU	
3.	Keyboard	
4.	Mouse	
5.	Mouse mat	
6.	CPU	
7.	Disk drive	
8.	Ergonomics	
9.	Printer	
10.	Work station	
11.	RSI	
12.	Anti-glare filter	
13.	Footrest	
14.	Document holder	
15.	Radiation	
16.	Wristrest	
17.	WYSIWYG	
18.	Static	

 Reproduced from *Health and Safety Games for Trainers*, Graham Roberts-Phelps, Gower, Aldershot

📄 Test 8: Risk Assessment

Working in pairs or small groups, discuss and answer the following questions.

Question	Answer
1. Give a definition of 'risk assessment'.	
2. What is the purpose of carrying out a risk assessment?	
3. Define the words 'hazard' and 'risk'.	Hazard: Risk:
4. What groups of people do you need to consider when performing a risk assessment?	
5. List three pieces of legislation of which you need to be aware.	1. 2. 3.
6. Is it an employer's legal requirement to complete a risk assessment for all employees or only those working with significant hazards in higher risk areas?	(a) All employees (b) Only those employees working with significant hazards in higher risk areas
7. When implementing recommendations is cost an excuse for not implementing certain measures?	
8. List three benefits to the organization of carrying out proper risk assessment.	1. 2. 3.
9. List three benefits to employees of carrying out proper risk assessments.	1. 2. 3.
10. Are all electrical boards marked up correctly? If not, how can this be achieved?	

📄 Test 9: Safety for Managers

Working in pairs or small groups, discuss and answer the following questions.

Question	Answer
1. List three hazards with potential to cause harm in the workplace.	1. 2. 3.
2. List three common causes of accidents in the workplace.	1. 2. 3.
3. What is the difference between a 'hazard' and 'risk'?	
4. List three things to remember when lifting or picking up things.	1. 2. 3.
5. List three things you could check to do with electricity and electrical appliances.	1. 2. 3.
6. List three things that cause slips or trips in the workplace.	1. 2. 3.
7. List three things that employers are legally bound to do as regards health and safety at work.	1. 2. 3.
8. List three things that employees are legally bound to do as regards health and safety at work.	1. 2. 3.
9. Safety inspectors have right of entry, right to interview and take samples with or without an organization's permission.	True or False
10. List three pieces of recent EC legislation that may affect you.	1. 2. 3.

Reproduced from *Health and Safety Games for Trainers*, Graham Roberts-Phelps, Gower, Aldershot

📄 Test 10: Environmental Awareness

Working in pairs or small groups, discuss and answer the following questions.

Question	Answer
1. How many cars are scrapped in Britain each year?	(a) 250 000 (b) 500 000 (c) 1 million
2. How much sewage is pumped into Britain's seas, most of it untreated or partially filtered?	(a) 100 million gallons (227 million litres) (b) 300 million gallons (1 350 million litres) (c) 600 million gallons (2 700 million litres)
3. In the last 30 years what percentage of the world's rhinos have been killed for their horns?	(a) 85 per cent (b) 65 per cent (c) 55 per cent
4. How much water does the average Briton use in a year?	(a) 5 000 gallons (22 750 litres) (b) 10 000 gallons (45 500 litres) (c) 50 000 gallons (227 500 litres)
5. How much paper do the people of Britain put into their rubbish bins every week?	(a) 100 tons (100 000 kilograms) (b) 500 tons (500 000 kilograms) (c) 1 000 tons (1 million kilograms)
6. What percentage of household rubbish is made up of packaging?	(a) 30 per cent (b) 20 per cent (c) 10 per cent
7. What percentage of Britain's paper is thrown away without recycling?	(a) 25 per cent (b) 60 per cent (c) 75 per cent
8. According to government officials, what percentage of Britain's household rubbish could be reclaimed?	(a) 30 per cent (b) 60 per cent (c) 80 per cent

Question	Answer
9. What percentage of drinkable tap water is actually drunk?	(a) 50 per cent (b) 10 per cent (c) 1 per cent
10. What is the total mileage that the residents of Los Angeles drive every day?	(a) 150 million miles (250 million kilometres) (b) 100 million miles (160 million kilometres) (c) 50 million miles (80 million kilometres)
11. How far is the average car journey in Britain?	(a) 24 miles (39 kilometres) (b) 53 miles (85 kilometres) (c) six miles (10 kilometres)
12. How much fuel does the average car consume in its lifetime?	(a) 860 gallons (3 900 litres) (b) 1 680 gallons (7 650 litres) (c) 2 250 gallons (10 225 litres)

4. Self-assessment Questionnaires

Questionnaires 1–8

Trainer's notes

Outline	
Format:	**Individuals**
Type:	**Safety awareness questionnaires**
Time:	**20 minutes**
Resources:	**Handouts provided**

Objective

Use this activity at the beginning or towards the end of a course, to either introduce or reinforce key learning points. The purpose of this exercise is to establish delegates' knowledge and attitudes towards safety and to highlight some important skills.

Procedure

Distribute the handouts and ask each delegate to work through his or her questionnaire as honestly and accurately as possible. Review each in turn, discussing the issues arising. Note that any item given a 1 or 2 is not acceptable, delegates must give 3, 4 or 5 to ensure good safety standards.

📄 Questionnaire 1: Safety Awareness

Complete the following questionnaire, as honestly and accurately as you can. Rate your response to each statement on the following scale.

1 = Never, 2 = Sometimes, 3 = Usually, 4 = Often, 5 = Always

Statement	Response				
1. I consider safety issues before tackling a new job or task.	1	2	3	4	5
2. I encourage co-workers to take safety seriously.	1	2	3	4	5
3. I use safety guards and shields on machines and tools.	1	2	3	4	5
4. I am careful when using electricity.	1	2	3	4	5
5. I allow time to check things before I start something new.	1	2	3	4	5
6. I ask for help or advice when I am not sure of something.	1	2	3	4	5
7. I can accept constructive criticism about safety practices and my work.	1	2	3	4	5
8. I input my ideas into the safety planning and programmes.	1	2	3	4	5
9. I am especially cautious when dealing with chemicals.	1	2	3	4	5
10. I avoid taking short-cuts and cutting corners that may involve increasing the risk of an accident or injury.	1	2	3	4	5
11. I make sure that the area I am working in is organized and tidy.	1	2	3	4	5
12. If I feel tired or start making silly mistakes, I take a break or change tasks.	1	2	3	4	5
13. I avoid taking risks with other people's safety.	1	2	3	4	5
14. I am careful when lifting or moving objects.	1	2	3	4	5
15. I take regular exercise and stay fit.	1	2	3	4	5
16. I am careful of what I eat and avoid heavy meals during the day.	1	2	3	4	5
17. I avoid using alcohol, drugs or excessive medication.	1	2	3	4	5
18. I always use a seat belt when driving or as a passenger.	1	2	3	4	5

My score is _____ out of 90

Score:

75–90   Excellent   35–54   OK, but there is room for improvement
55–74   Very good   less than 35 points   Don't walk under too many ladders!

Reproduced from *Health and Safety Games for Trainers*, Graham Roberts-Phelps, Gower, Aldershot

📄 Questionnaire 2: Fire Safety

Complete the following questionnaire, as honestly and accurately as you can. Rate your response to each statement on the following scale.

1 = Never, 2 = Sometimes, 3 = Usually, 4 = Often, 5 = Always

Statement	Response				
1. I can list the correct procedure for calling the fire brigade.	1	2	3	4	5
2. I know the names of the fire wardens and their responsibilities.	1	2	3	4	5
3. I know where the nearest fire exit or escape is in this room.	1	2	3	4	5
4. I know where the fire exit or escape is in my normal place of work.	1	2	3	4	5
5. I know whether the fire alarm is an alarm bell or a siren.	1	2	3	4	5
6. I know where the fire alarm is located in this room.	1	2	3	4	5
7. I know where the fire alarm is located in my normal place of work.	1	2	3	4	5
8. I can say when I did the last check to make sure that exits and corridors were not blocked.	1	2	3	4	5
9. I know how often I would normally check.	1	2	3	4	5
10. I can state what the essential information is to give when calling the fire brigade.	1	2	3	4	5
11. I can list the precise steps to take if I hear the fire alarm sound.	1	2	3	4	5
12. I can list where the nearest fire extinguishers are located in this room.	1	2	3	4	5
13. I can list where the fire extinguishers are located in my normal place of work.	1	2	3	4	5
14. I can list the precise steps to take when operating a fire extinguisher (of the sort that I have in my workplace).	1	2	3	4	5

My score is _____ out of 70

Score:

56–70 points   Excellent
41–55 points   Very good
29–40 points   OK, but there is room for improvement
less than 28 points   Don't walk under too many ladders!

Reproduced from *Health and Safety Games for Trainers*, Graham Roberts-Phelps, Gower, Aldershot

📄 Questionnaire 3: Safe Manual Handling

Complete the following questionnaire, as honestly and accurately as you can. Rate your response to each statement on the following scale.

1 = Never, 2 = Sometimes, 3 = Usually, 4 = Often, 5 = Always

Statement	Response				
1. I consider avoiding manual handling wherever possible.	1	2	3	4	5
2. If I see someone lifting, carrying or loading in a way that is *not* particularly safe or clever, I will point it out to them.	1	2	3	4	5
3. I assess the risk of each handling operation that can't be avoided.	1	2	3	4	5
4. I use mechanical equipment wherever possible, such as by using trucks, hoists and trolleys.	1	2	3	4	5
5. I try to make loads smaller, lighter or easier to grasp.	1	2	3	4	5
6. I make sure that my work area is kept clear and uncluttered.	1	2	3	4	5
7. I can accept constructive criticism about lifting practices at work.	1	2	3	4	5
8. I think through lifting tasks in advance.	1	2	3	4	5
9. I am careful to move my feet rather than twisting.	1	2	3	4	5
10. I wear appropriate protective clothing, such as gloves and shoes.	1	2	3	4	5
11. I read the outside of boxes to check the weight and contents.	1	2	3	4	5
12. If I feel tired or start making mistakes, I take a break or change tasks.	1	2	3	4	5
13. When lifting objects, I check for the centre of gravity before lifting.	1	2	3	4	5
14. I feel able to say 'no' to lifting things that are too heavy for me.	1	2	3	4	5

My score is _____ out of 70

Score:

56–70 points   Excellent
41–55 points   Very good
29–40 points   OK, but there is room for improvement
less than 28 points   A manual handling accident waiting to happen!

    Reproduced from *Health and Safety Games for Trainers*, Graham Roberts-Phelps, Gower, Aldershot

📄 Questionnaire 4: Safety Awareness for Managers

Complete the following questionnaire, as honestly and accurately as you can. Rate your response to each statement on the following scale.

1 = Never, 2 = Sometimes, 3 = Usually, 4 = Often, 5 = Always

Statement	Response
1. I make sure that the company's health and safety policy is implemented and understood by all staff, visitors and contractors or temporary workers.	1 2 3 4 5
2. I make sure sure all staff are fully aware of their legal responsibilities with regard to health and safety at work, or while on company business.	1 2 3 4 5
3. I make sure that any special directives or controls, such as COSHH or PPE, are properly carried out.	1 2 3 4 5
4. I make sure that all staff are properly trained to an agreed or recognized standard.	1 2 3 4 5
5. I make sure job specifications and demands are within safety guidelines.	1 2 3 4 5
6. I work with staff in resolving safety issues and providing a link between them and the safety officer.	1 2 3 4 5
7. The staff and I attend appropriate meetings where health and safety is discussed.	1 2 3 4 5
8. I make sure that **all** accidents and injuries are reported according to procedures.	1 2 3 4 5

My score is _____ out of 40

Score:

33–40 points	Excellent, probably a very safe work environment
25–32 points	Very good, a really high level of safety awareness
16–24 points	Okay, but there is room for improvement
less than 15 points	An accident waiting to happen!

📄 Questionnaire 5: Environmental Awareness

Complete the following questionnaire, as honestly and accurately as you can. Rate your response to each statement on the following scale.

1 = Never, 2 = Sometimes, 3 = Usually, 4 = Often, 5 = Always

Statement	Response				
1. I (or others) recycle newspapers and waste paper using local recycling facilities.	1	2	3	4	5
2. I (or others) recycle bottles, plastic and tins.	1	2	3	4	5
3. I (or others) use two sides of the paper when writing reports or memos.	1	2	3	4	5
4. I (or others) use the reverse side of single-sided paper for scrap and note paper.	1	2	3	4	5
5. I (or others) am careful in selecting suppliers to check that the content of products are as environmentally sound as possible.	1	2	3	4	5
6. I (or others) use the phone instead of sending a letter or memo whenever practical.	1	2	3	4	5
7. I (or others) choose products that have the least packaging.	1	2	3	4	5
8. I (or others) drive in a manner that uses less fuel.	1	2	3	4	5
9. I (or others) use public transport whenever possible.	1	2	3	4	5
10. I (or others) walk or cycle for short journeys.	1	2	3	4	5
11. I (or others) input environmental ideas into planning and meetings.	1	2	3	4	5
12. I (or others) take steps to reduce mileage travelled on business.	1	2	3	4	5
13. Whenever possible, I (or others) source products and supplies from local suppliers to avoid unnecessary distribution.	1	2	3	4	5
14. Waste products produced by the organization are treated and disposed of properly.	1	2	3	4	5
15. Whenever possible, I (or others) repair or renew items to avoid unnecessary extra consumption.	1	2	3	4	5

Reproduced from *Health and Safety Games for Trainers*, Graham Roberts-Phelps, Gower, Aldershot

📄 Questionnaire 6: Risk Awareness

Complete the following questionnaire, as honestly and accurately as you can. Rate your response to each statement on the following scale.

1 = Never, 2 = Sometimes, 3 = Usually, 4 = Often, 5 = Always

Statement	Response
1. I can give an example of a significant hazard from my own work environment and the level of risk associated with this.	1　2　3　4　5
2. I know how often I should complete a risk assessment.	1　2　3　4　5
3. I can list three sets of legislation of which I need to be aware.	1　2　3　4　5
4. I spot new or increased hazards in my work and do something about them.	1　2　3　4　5
5. I understand the meaning of 'risk assessment'.	1　2　3　4　5
6. I have evaluated the risks arising from hazards and have decided that existing precautions are adequate.	1　2　3　4　5
7. Most of the hazards I have identified are low risk.	1　2　3　4　5
8. I understand how to assess that my company is meeting all legal standards.	1　2　3　4　5
9. I speak to other employees or their representatives to see if they have noticed risks that are not immediately obvious.	1　2　3　4　5
10. If I need to make improvements to increase safety, I first look at the hazard to see if I can do the job in a different way.	1　2　3　4　5

My score is _____ out of 50

Score:

41–50 points　Excellent
31–40 points　Very good
21–30 points　OK
less than 20 points　Room for improvement!

📄 Questionnaire 7: Display Screen Equipment

Complete the following questionnaire, as honestly and accurately as you can. Rate your response to each statement on the following scale.

1 = Never, 2 = Sometimes, 3 = Usually, 4 = Often, 5 = Always

Statement	Response				
1. My screen image is bright and clear.	1	2	3	4	5
2. My monitor swivels and tilts easily.	1	2	3	4	5
3. The symbols on my keyboard are legible.	1	2	3	4	5
4. My desk is sufficiently tidy and well organized to allow for flexibility in positioning equipment.	1	2	3	4	5
5. The height and back of my work chair are adjustable.	1	2	3	4	5
6. I do not get any glare or reflection from light fittings, windows, etc, on my display screen.	1	2	3	4	5
7. The heat emission from my computer equipment is dissipated adequately.	1	2	3	4	5
8. I have received training in the use of my work station.	1	2	3	4	5
9. Guidance has been given and I understand the arrangements for eyesight testing.	1	2	3	4	5
10. If I am wearing spectacles or contact lenses, I have been advised of their suitability for display screen work.	1	2	3	4	5

My score is _____ out of 50

Score:

41–50 points   Excellent
31–40 points   Very good
21–30 points   OK
less than 20 points   Room for improvement!

   Reproduced from *Health and Safety Games for Trainers*, Graham Roberts-Phelps, Gower, Aldershot

📄 Questionnaire 8: COSHH Safety

Complete the following questionnaire, as honestly and accurately as you can. Rate your response to each statement on the following scale.

1 = Never, 2 = Sometimes, 3 = Usually, 4 = Often, 5 = Always

Statement	Response
1. Hazardous substances that are either stored or used on the premises have been identified and COSHH data sheets obtained.	1 2 3 4 5
2. All the hazardous substances have been established as essential to the task or function for which they are used.	1 2 3 4 5
3. All necessary safety precautions have been established for each hazardous substance.	1 2 3 4 5
4. I understand that all necessary water and ventilation systems have been installed as safety precautions.	1 2 3 4 5
5. I have received training on the tasks I perform and the use of hazardous substances.	No = 1 Yes = 5
6. I have received training on the remedial actions to be taken in the event of an accident, spillage or other dangerous occurrence.	1 2 3 4 5
7. Safety precautions are in place for the removal of used substances.	1 2 3 4 5
8. I have all the personal protective equipment necessary in case I come into contact with a hazardous substance.	No = 1 Yes = 5
9. I understand that all hazardous substances are clearly marked and colour coded for the substance stored.	1 2 3 4 5
10. Warning signs are in place close to the hazardous substances being stored.	1 2 3 4 5

My score is _____ out of 50

Score:

41–50 points   Excellent
31–40 points   Very good
21–30 points   OK
less than 20 points   Room for improvement!

5. Workplace Assessment Questionnaires

Questionnaires 1–10

Trainer's notes

Outline	
Format:	*Individuals*
Type:	*Action planning*
Time:	*15–20 minutes, plus discussion*
Resources:	*Handouts provided*

Objective

This activity will identify areas for improvement and help develop solutions. It will establish delegates' knowledge and attitudes towards safety and to highlight some important skills.

Procedure

This is best done during or before a training session. Distribute the handouts to the delegates and ask them each to picture or visit their normal place of work and complete the questionnaire accurately and fully.

Review each point carefully, discussing examples and possible solutions. During the discussion, try to establish what are the three most important points to be considered in each assessment.

📄 Questionnaire 1: Workplace Assessment

Visiting or picturing your workplace, complete the following questionnaire, as honestly and accurately as you can. Mark each question with a ✓ as yes or no.

Question	Yes	No
1. Are workers free from draughts or excessive air movement?		
2. If the workplace sometimes gets too warm, have steps been taken to reduce the temperature?		
3. Are thermometers available to allow staff to check temperatures?		
4. Is the temperature in the workplace normally controlled at a reasonable level?		
5. If extremes of cold cannot be avoided, are staff provided with suitable protective clothing?		
6. Are the floor coverings adequate?		
7. If portable heating appliances are used, are they safe to use in the workplace and carefully placed?		
8. Are heating and ventilation facilities regularly inspected and serviced?		
9. Is there sufficient fresh air in the workplace and is it free from fumes and odours?		

Reproduced from *Health and Safety Games for Trainers*, Graham Roberts-Phelps, Gower, Aldershot

Questionnaire 2: Display Screen Equipment

Visiting or picturing your workplace, complete the following questionnaire as honestly and accurately as you can. Mark each question with a ✓ as yes or no.

Question	Yes	No
1. Is your work desk large enough to allow flexibility and comfort?		
2. Is your chair stable and the right type?		
3. Does your chair allow you freedom of movement?		
4. Is the height of the chair adjustable?		
5. Is the screen image stable?		
6. When adjusted, is the screen image clear and acceptable?		
7. Is there space in front of the keyboard to support your hands?		
8. Are the symbols on the keys legible?		
9. Is there a document holder available, if required?		
10. Is there enough space for comfort on the desk top?		
11. Is the working area free from glare?		
12. Do you suffer any aches and pains in your arms, neck, hands, shoulders, etc.?		
13. Are sufficient breaks away from the keyboard provided?		

Reproduced from *Health and Safety Games for Trainers*, Graham Roberts-Phelps, Gower, Aldershot

📄 Questionnaire 3: Electric Safety

Visiting or picturing your workplace, complete the following questionnaire as honestly and accurately as you can. Mark each question with a ✓ as yes or no.

Question	Yes	No
1. Are staff given suitable and sufficient training, instruction and information on the use of all equipment and the task for which it is used?		
2. Have all electrical installations been tested in accordance with the current Regulations?		
3. Is a permit to work system in operation to prevent those doing work being put at risk by others?		
4. Are the doors of electrical switchrooms fitted with 'DANGER 240/415 volts' notices?		
5. Has the recommended testing period been entered onto the Test Certificate?		
6. Is there a notice regarding electrical shocks displayed by the switchgear?		
7. Are all appliance test records available?		
8. In situations where persons might fall or trip, or where risks are apparent, is secure fencing provided and are notices visible?		

Reproduced from *Health and Safety Games for Trainers*, Graham Roberts-Phelps, Gower, Aldershot

📄 Questionnaire 4: Safety for Managers

Visiting or picturing your workplace, complete the following questionnaire as honestly and accurately as you can. Mark each question with a ✓ as yes or no.

Question	Yes	No
1. Do you consult and involve your staff and the safety representatives regularly in discussing health and safety issues?		
2. Does your safety policy clearly specify people's responsibilities?		
3. Have you listed some of the responsibilities that you allocate to people for health and safety issues (e.g. first aiders and fire wardens)?		
4. Do your staff feel they have enough information about the risks in their work and how to take preventative steps?		
5. At what stage do you consider health and safety issues when new work routines, equipment or procedures are introduced: before? during? after?		
6. Are all noise precautions regularly checked and records kept?		
7. Have noise checks been performed?		
8. Do you know how many accidents or near misses occur at work in your department/company every year?		
9. Do you pay attention to changes in legislation?		
10. Are you implementing the standards you set yourself and are they effective?		
11. Do you have a formal system for reporting accidents?		

📄 Questionnaire 5: Fire Safety

Visiting or picturing your workplace, complete the following questionnaire as honestly and accurately as you can. Mark each question with a ✔ as yes or no.

Fire Safety is a specialised subject and the professional advice of the Fire Prevention Officer of the local Fire Authority should be obtained in all circumstances.

Question	Yes	No
1. Are sufficient and adequate fire fighting appliances available?		
2. Are portable fire fighting appliances of the correct type?		
3. If an automatic fire alarm system exists, is it regularly tested and maintained?		
4. Are records of fire alarm tests and maintenance kept? Are they up-to-date?		
5. Are all fire fighting installations and appliances regularly tested and maintained?		
6. Are flammable liquids, chemicals, gases, alcohol, etc. stored in accordance with the regulations?		
7. Are all electrical and mechanical plant rooms free from unnecessary stored material?		
8. Is there a system of automatic smoke detection on all escape routes?		
9. Are all necessary fire signs displayed in appropriate places?		
10. Are fire evacuation drills held periodically?		
11. Are records kept of staff fire training?		
12. Have all practical steps been taken to eliminate smoking in the workplace?		

Reproduced from *Health and Safety Games for Trainers*, Graham Roberts-Phelps, Gower, Aldershot

📄 Questionnaire 6: Office Safety

Visiting or picturing your workplace, complete the following questionnaire as honestly and accurately as you can. Mark each question with a ✓ as yes or no.

Question	Yes	No
1. Are the noise levels of all operations and equipment below the noise threshold?		
2. Have reasonable and adequate steps been taken to reduce or eliminate noisy operations?		
3. Are all relevant safety signs and notices clear and easy to understand?		
4. Are suitable sanitary conveniences provided in accessible places?		
5. Are sufficient and adequate sanitary conveniences provided for both men and women and are the rooms properly ventilated and illuminated?		
6. Are sufficient washing facilities available in the vicinity of all sanitary conveniences and changing rooms?		
7. Is the office temperature acceptable/comfortable most of the time?		
8. Where applicable, are there special sanitary facilities for the disabled?		
9. Is the air quality acceptable?		
10. Is there adequate light and is glare controlled?		
11. Are cables tidy and away from thoroughfares?		
12. Is sufficient training and information given to workers on the use of the office facilities?		
13. Are thoroughfares clear from bump and trip hazards?		

📄 Questionnaire 7: Environmental Awareness

Visiting or picturing your workplace, complete the following questionnaire as honestly and accurately as you can. Mark each question with a ✓ as yes or no.

Question	Yes	No
1. Is the temperature in the workplace controlled at a reasonable level (minimum 16°C)?		
2. If extremes of temperature cannot be avoided, are the workers provided with suitable protective outfits/clothing?		
3. Are thermometers available at convenient positions to enable staff to check temperatures?		
4. Are products of combustion discharged safely, away from the workplace?		
5. Is sufficient fresh air introduced into the workplace by either natural or mechanical means?		
6. Is fresh air that is introduced free from impurities, fumes or odours?		
7. Are workers free from draughts or air movement?		

Reproduced from *Health and Safety Games for Trainers*, Graham Roberts-Phelps, Gower, Aldershot

Questionnaire 8: Manual Handling

Visiting or picturing your workplace, complete the following questionnaire as honestly and accurately as you can. Mark each question with a ✓ as yes or no.

Question	Yes	No
1. Have staff been trained on manual handling techniques and rules?		
2. Is it practical to mechanize or automate any tasks at reasonable cost?		
3. Is it reasonable to avoid moving heavy loads?		
4. Is there stated permission for rest and/or recovery periods?		
5. Are instructions given to workers not to lift certain loads without help or supervision?		
6. In the normal working environment, is good posture used?		
7. Is there ample space to allow good posture?		
8. Is the floor and walk area of good quality?		
9. Is the floor and work surface level?		
10. Is the working temperature reasonable?		
11. Is the lighting level sufficient?		
12. Is the air movement reasonable?		
13. Has training been given to all workers on health and safety matters relative to lifting tasks and also the use of all equipment and tools?		
14. Are gloves, boots and other protective aids provided?		

Questionnaire 9: Hazardous Substances

Visiting or picturing your workplace, complete the following questionnaire as honestly and accurately as you can. Mark each question with a ✓ as yes or no.

Question	Yes	No
1. Have all hazardous substances stored or used on the premises been listed and (COSHH) data sheets obtained?		
2. Has the use of each substance been considered as essential? Are safer alternatives available?		
3. Have all necessary safety precautions been established for each hazardous substance?		
4. Are all correct hazard warning signs in place close to the substances in use?		
5. Are all vessels, bags and wrappings that contain hazardous substances clearly marked for the substance stored?		
6. Are all necessary antidotes or neutralizing agents available in close proximity to the hazardous substance?		
7. Is all necessary personal protective equipment/clothing available to all workers who use or come into contact with a hazardous substance? Is the clothing/equipment worn and used correctly at all times?		
8. Has full information been given to workers on the hazardous substances that they use or come into contact with, and on the associated risks.		

Reproduced from *Health and Safety Games for Trainers*, Graham Roberts-Phelps, Gower, Aldershot

Questionnaire 10: Personal Protective Equipment

Visiting or picturing your workplace, complete the following questionnaire as honestly and accurately as possible. Mark each question with a ✓ as yes or no.

Question	Yes	No
1. Has suitable personal protective equipment been issued to workers who are exposed to conditions that require special work clothing?		
2. Does the personal protective equipment take into account ergonomic requirements?		
3. Does the personal protective equipment fit correctly, if necessary after adjustment?		
4. Does the personal protective equipment comply with current British or EEC standards?		
5. If personal protective equipment is not issued on a personal basis, do workers have clear instructions where to obtain it?		
6. If more than one item of personal protective equipment is to be worn, are the items compatible?		
7. Have the workers been instructed to change personal protective equipment that is past its stated life?		

6.   Ice-breakers

Quizzes 1–3   Trainer's Notes

Quiz 1   Safety Signs Handout

Quiz 2   First Aid Handout

Quiz 3   Health and Safety Jargon Handout

Word Challenge 1 and 2
   Trainer's Notes
   Handout 1
   Handout 2

Caption Competition
   Trainer's Notes
   Handout

Learning Assignment, Accident or Incident Review
   Trainer's Notes
   Notes on Reporting Injuries and Other Events
   Handout

Flip Chart Exercise 1   Driving Forward For Safety
   Trainer's Notes
   Handout

Flip Chart Exercise 2   Safety Iceberg Analysis
   Trainer's Notes
   Handout

Flip Chart Exercise 3   Mnemonic Challenge
   Trainer's Notes
   Handout

Flip Chart Exercise 4   Safety Competence Chart
   Trainer's Notes
   Handout

Quizzes 1–3

Trainer's notes

Outline	
Format:	*Pairs/small groups*
Type:	*Ice-breakers*
Time:	*15 minutes, plus discussion*
Resources:	*Handout provided*

Objective

To test and reinforce safety knowledge.

Procedure

Give the delegates the handout provided and ask them to work in pairs/small groups. Allow them 15 minutes to complete the quiz and then review the answers.

📄 Quiz 1: Safety Signs

How many of the following signs do you know? Write the meaning underneath each sign.

1. 2. 3. 4.

_____ _____ _____ _____

5. 6. 7. 8.

_____ _____ _____ _____

9. 10. 11. 12.

_____ _____ _____ _____

13. 14.

_____ _____

 Reproduced from *Health and Safety Games for Trainers*, Graham Roberts-Phelps, Gower, Aldershot

📄 Quiz 2: First Aid

In pairs or small groups, review the list of the accidents or injuries below. Against each, write exactly what you would do if you were first on the scene.

Injury/accident	Immediate action
1. Badly cut and bleeding hand	
2. Broken glass in foot	
3. Inhaled car fumes	
4. Swallowed white spirit	
5. Suspected epileptic fit	
6. Fainting	
7. Fall from ladder	
8. Motorbike accident, person still conscious	
9. Bump on head from fall	
10. Suspected broken ankle from trip down the stairs	
11. Convulsive fit	

📄 Quiz 3: Health and Safety Jargon

In pairs or small groups, review the list of safety terms below and complete their definitions.

Safety term	Definition
1. Hazard	
2. Risk	
3. COSHH	
4. PPE	
5. RSI	
6. Risk assessment	
7. Carcinogen	
8. Tinnitus	
9. Dermatitis	
10. White finger	
11. Sciatica	
12. VDU	
13. EEC Standard	
14. Recycle	
15. CPU	
16. LPG	
17. HSE	
18. Ozone	
19. CFC	

Reproduced from *Health and Safety Games for Trainers*, Graham Roberts-Phelps, Gower, Aldershot

Word Challenge 1 and 2

Trainer's notes

Outline	
Format:	**Pairs**
Type:	**Ice-breakers**
Time:	**5 minutes**
Resources:	**Handout provided**

Objective

A fun way to start or end a session.

Procedure

Give the delegates the handout provided. Ask them to work in pairs and allow them 5 minutes.

📄 Word Challenge 1

Working in pairs, find as many three letter words as possible in the following word.

ACCIDENT

Reproduced from *Health and Safety Games for Trainers*, Graham Roberts-Phelps, Gower, Aldershot

📄 Word Challenge 2

Working in pairs, find as many three letter words as possible in the following words.

RISK ASSESSMENT

Caption Competition

Trainer's notes

Outline	
Format:	*Pairs*
Type:	*Ice-breakers*
Time:	*15 minutes*
Resources:	*Handout provided*

Objective

A fun way to start or end a session.

Procedure

Give the delegates the handout provided. Ask them to work in pairs and allow them 15 minutes.

📄 Caption Competition

Working in pairs, review the following pictures and see if you can come up with humorous health and safety related captions.

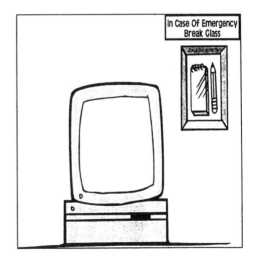

Reproduced from *Health and Safety Games for Trainers*, Graham Roberts-Phelps, Gower, Aldershot

Learning Assignment, Accident or Incident Review

Trainer's notes

Outline	
Format:	**Small groups**
Type:	**Discussion/problem solving**
Time:	**20 minutes, plus discussion**
Resources:	**Handouts provided**

Objective

To instruct participants in the correct procedures in the event of an accident or incident.

Procedure

Hand out the 'Notes on Reporting Injuries and Other Events'.

Ask delegates to review the notes and then on the 'Accident or Incident Review' Handout to make a step-by-step checklist of what they should do if an accident, near-miss or incident happens. They should consider what actions need to take place afterwards to ensure causes are identified and lessons are learnt.

After 20 minutes gather responses and discuss.

📄 Notes on Reporting Injuries and Other Events

RIDDOR applies to all employers and the self-employed and covers everyone at work.

Main Points

You must:

- notify your inspector immediately, normally by telephone, if anybody dies, receives a major injury or is seriously affected by, for example an electric shock or poisoning;

- notify your inspector immediately if there is a dangerous occurrence, for example a fire or explosion which stops work for more than 24 hours, or an overturned crane;

- confirm in writing within seven days of the accident on form F2508;

- report within seven days (on form F2508) injuries which keep an employee off work or unable to do his or her normal job for more than three days;

- report (on form F2508A) certain diseases suffered by workers who do specified types of work as soon as possible on learning about the illness;

- if you supply, fill or import flammable gas in reusable containers, notify the Health and Safety Executive immediately of any death or injury connected in any way with the gas supplied;

- keep details of the incident in a dedicated file.

Investigating Events

When an accident happens, you should:

- take any action required to deal with the immediate risks, for example first aid, put out the fire, isolate any danger or fence off the area;

- assess the level and kind of investigation needed – if you have to disturb the site, take photographs and measurements first;

- investigate to find out what happened and why;

- take steps to stop something similar happening again;

- look at near misses and property damage – often it is only by chance that someone was not injured;

- learn from the experience – what changes do you need to make to your accident procedures?

First Aid

You must have:

- an appointed person who can take charge in an emergency;

- a first-aid box;

- notices telling people where to find the first-aid box and the appointed person;

- a trained first-aider and a first-aid room if your work gives rise to special hazards, for example using a particularly toxic material.

Reproduced from *Health and Safety Games for Trainers*, Graham Roberts-Phelps, Gower, Aldershot

📄 Learning Assignment, Accident or Incident Review

Review the 'Notes on Reporting Injuries and Other Events'. Draw up a step-by-step checklist on what you should do if an accident, near miss or incident happens.

1. _____ ❑

2. _____ ❑

3. _____ ❑

4. _____ ❑

5. _____ ❑

6. _____ ❑

7. _____ ❑

8. _____ ❑

List what actions need to take place to ensure that causes are identified and lessons learnt.

_____

_____

_____

_____

_____

_____

_____

Flip Chart Exercise 1: Driving Forward for Safety

Trainer's notes

```
Outline
Format:        Pairs or small groups
Type:          Energizer
Time:          15–20 minutes, plus discussion
Resources:     Handout provided, flip chart
```

Objective

To identify issues regarding implementing changes to safety standards or work practices.

Procedure

Give the handouts to the pairs or small groups and copy the image onto a flip chart page.

Ask the pairs or groups to summarize the forces at work in a given situation as either driving forces or restraining forces, that is, those that either move forward or hold back the implementation of changes to safety standards of work practices.

After 15–20 minutes, gather the responses onto your flip chart and discuss how best to remove or reduce restraining forces.

📄 Flip Chart Exercise 1: Driving Forward for Safety

Identify the Driving Forces and the Restraining Forces.

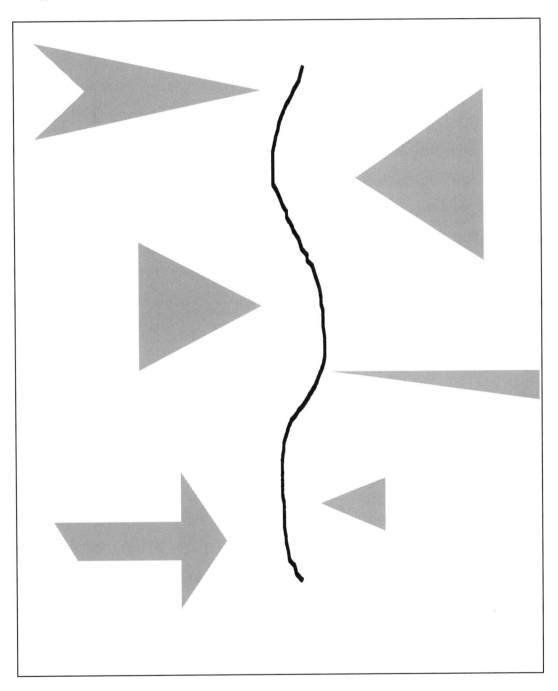

Reproduced from *Health and Safety Games for Trainers*, Graham Roberts-Phelps, Gower, Aldershot   81

Flip Chart Exercise 2: Safety Iceberg Analysis

Trainer's notes

```
Outline
Format:      Small groups
Type:        Discussion/problem solver
Time:        15–20 minutes, plus discussion
Resources:   Handout provided, flip chart
```

Objective

To develop a practical approach to solving health and safety problems or weak spots.

Procedure

Give the handouts to the groups and copy the image onto a flip chart page.

Define clearly one or more health and safety issue/s that the group is to address or analyse. Ask the groups to identify all of the (hidden) causes behind it and then all of the ways in which the issue might affect them at work without their being aware of it.

After 15–20 minutes, gather the responses and discuss.

📑 Flip Chart Exercise 2: Safety Iceberg Analysis

Problems are like icebergs – you only see a small part on the surface, but there are many causes and issues underlying them.

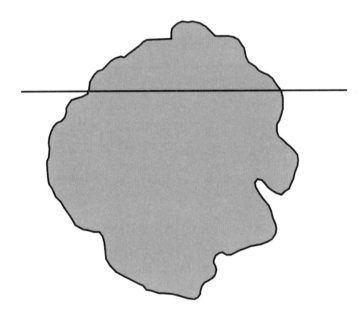

Flip Chart Exercise 3: Mnemonic Challenge

Trainer's notes

Outline	
Format:	*Pairs or small groups*
Type:	*Energizer*
Time:	*10 minutes, plus discussion*
Resources:	*Handout provided, flip chart*

Objective

To remember and summarize key safety points. As well as being an intriguing mental puzzle, mnemonics can act as a useful memory hook, for example 'backache' for a manual handling course.

Procedure

Give the handouts to the groups or pairs and ask them to select a word associated or related with the safety training topic and create a mnemonic that contains key points.

After ten minutes gather the responses on your flip chart and display and discuss as required.

📄 Flip Chart Exercise 3: Mnemonic Challenge

Create a mnemonic which is relevant to the course and contains some ideas from it.

F
U
N

Flip
Up
Notes

Flip Chart Exercise 4: Safety Competence Chart

Trainer's notes

Outline	
Format:	*Small groups*
Type:	*Energizer*
Time:	*10–15 minutes, plus discussion*
Resources:	*Handout provided, flip chart*

Objective

To clearly define safety competence levels for any job, task or process.

Procedure

Give the handouts to the groups. Ask them to specify a job, task or process that is relevant to their training course and identify key **knowledge** elements, **skills** and techniques, **attitudes** and day-to-day **behaviours** that combine together to represent 'competence' at that job, task or process.

After 10–15 minutes, gather their responses by copying them onto your flip chart and display and discuss as required.

📄 Flip Chart Exercise 4: Safety Competence Chart

Job, task or process ...

*Identify key **Skills**, **Attitudes**, **Behaviours** and **Knowledge** that are needed for a person to be considered 'competent' for the job, task or process.*

Knowledge	Skills
Attitudes	Behaviours

Flip Chart Exercise 5: Safety Parking Place

Trainer's notes

```
Outline
Format:        Pairs or small groups
Type:          Energizer
Time:          10–15 minutes, plus discussion
Resources:     Handout provided, flip chart
```

Objective

This can be used during the course to post any issues questions, observations or concerns about the subject under discussion or related topics.

Procedure

Give the handouts to the groups or pairs and ask them to discuss their ideas or questions regarding safety practices, policy or resources in their jobs or work area, and to list them.

After 10–15 minutes, gather their responses onto your flip chart and display and discuss as required.

Flip Chart Exercise 5: Safety Parking Place

Please park your issues, questions, concerns or queries on safety practices, policy or resources here.

Flip Chart Exercise 6: Safety Pictogram

Trainer's notes

<table>
<tr><td colspan="2">Outline</td></tr>
<tr><td>Format:</td><td>Small groups</td></tr>
<tr><td>Type:</td><td>Energizer</td></tr>
<tr><td>Time:</td><td>10 minutes</td></tr>
<tr><td>Resources:</td><td>Handout provided, flip chart</td></tr>
</table>

Objective

This can be used towards the end of the course to summarize key points.

Procedure

Give the handouts to the groups and ask them to draw one or more illustrations or pictures to summarize what has just been covered during the session. These can be copied onto flip charts and displayed and discussed.

Flip Chart Exercise 6: Safety Pictogram

Summarize one or more key points from the course using pictures, icons or graphics.

Hazards and Risks

Trainer's notes

Outline	
Format:	*Pairs/small groups*
Type:	*Energizer*
Time:	*15 minutes, plus discussion*
Resources:	*Handout provided*

Objective

To reflect on hazards in the workplace and to assess their risks (chance of happening).

Procedure

Ask delegates to list the top ten hazards in their workplace on the handout provided. They should then rate their risk (chance of happening) as low, medium or high.

After 15 minutes, gather responses and discuss.

📑 Hazards and Risks

List ten hazards that exist in your workplace, and use a ✓ to rate their risk (chance of happening) as either low, medium or high.

Hazard	High risk	Medium risk	Low risk
1.			
2.			
3.			
4.			
5.			
6.			
7.			
8.			
9.			
10.			

Safe Manual Handling Summary

Trainer's notes

Outline	
Format:	*Pairs/small groups*
Type:	*Energizer*
Time:	*10–15 minutes, plus discussion*
Resources:	*Handout provided, flip chart*

Objective

To summarize the main points of the safe manual handling advice offered.

Procedure

Ask the delegates to read through the Safe Manual Handling Summary provided. After reviewing the notes, they should design a poster, advert, verse or single page to represent the main points.

After 10–15 minutes, display as appropriate and discuss.

Safe Manual Handling Summary

Here is the simple, but very important sequence to follow when lifting or moving objects by hand. These six steps will ensure that you lift things not only correctly but also in a way that is as safe as possible and which minimizes the risk of injury to yourself and others. They will also ensure that you will be working within manual handling safety guidelines and regulations that are set down not only by your organization, but also by the manual handling safety authorities and regulators.

1. Pause and take position

The very first step, regardless of what you are lifting or how heavy it is, is to take a few seconds to think carefully about how you are going to lift it, the route you are taking when you are carrying it, where you are actually going to put it and, most importantly perhaps, how to position yourself correctly over, around or next to the object. Most back injuries and discomfort are caused by an incorrect position that puts undue strain on the muscles or the back.

The position of your feet is particularly important and they should be placed normal width apart so you have a solid stance. You should also be as close to the object as possible.

If there are things that need to be moved or adjusted, or if there are lifting aids that you need to fetch, then do this before beginning the operation.

For instance, we all occasionally kick the door open whilst carrying objects, this is increasing the risk of a manual handling accident or injury happening. Now that you have attended this training course, performing this kind of action could be deemed as unsafe working practice. This means that if you did do this, and were involved in a manual handling accident or injury, the liability would be yours because you should have known better. Of course, what we should do is to prop open the door before beginning the lift.

2. Bend (with your knees not your back)

Part of positioning is to make sure you get 'underneath' the load. This means that you bend your knees and get a grip, that is you actually hold the load or the object as much as you can underneath the main centre of gravity.

Safe lifting means lifting with your legs, not your back.

Bend your knees, keep your back straight and lower yourself down to the same level as the object you want to lift.

Then, when you do lift, you will be able to push up with your legs, keeping your back straight all the time.

3. Grip

If you are lifting a box or a reasonably square object, as is very common, your hands should be underneath the corners avoiding any sharp edges or any loose materials and have a firm secure grip.

Before lifting, or at least before you take the main weight, test your grip fully. Use your grip to lean the weight into your body making sure that its centre of gravity, or the heaviest part of the load, is closest to you.

If you need to wear protective gloves, either to get a better grip or to protect your hands, it is essential that you do this.

You may also need to consider if you are wearing the correct footwear. This footwear is to give you grip and to protect your feet if there is a dropped load.

4. Look up

When you are lifting, moving or carrying an object, it is important that you keep looking all around you as you do so. This makes sure that you look where you are going and that no-one walks or bumps into you, and importantly, it ensures that you lift correctly.

Keep your head upright and your back straight. If you begin to drop your head, this may cause your back to bend or curve, putting undue strain on the ligaments and muscles of the lower back in particular, so it is important that you keep your head up and your shoulders back.

Steer with your eyes – look not at the floor or where you have been, but ahead in the direction you are moving and at where you are putting your feet.

5. Lift with your legs

Your legs are the largest muscle group in the body, you only have to look at a weight-lifter or athlete to see that is true. When a weight-lifter or body-builder becomes skilled at lifting very heavy weights, it is usually their legs that become the biggest or the strongest body part.

In contrast, our back muscles, and our back structure in particular, are extremely complex and extremely fragile. We can damage our back very easily and with the smallest load. When you take the weight of an object, you must do so with your legs.

If you are lifting an object from the floor, rather than bending over and lifting with your arms, it is much safer to bend your knees crouched down over the object, get a secure grip and then lift up straightening your knees and pushing up as you do so. When moving or carrying items make sure that the weight is resting with your legs and not on your back.

6. Hold the load close

This step is particularly simple and almost deceptively obvious, but is vitally important to remember. The closer you hold the load or the object to yourself, the less strain you put on your back. Always make sure you have the heaviest part of whatever you are lifting towards you and pull it as close to you as possible.

Often, people report strains and injuries when trying to lift items which they do not want to touch their clothing for some reason. For instance, when unloading

    Reproduced from *Health and Safety Games for Trainers*, Graham Roberts-Phelps, Gower, Aldershot

gardening materials from the boot of the car, we will deliberately hold them away from us, in doing so risking painful or disabling injuries.

Weight guidelines

Although the amount that we can actually lift will, of course, vary from individual to individual and depend on what we are lifting or moving and the conditions or environment in which we are moving them, there are general guidelines.

When lifting a box from the floor to a bench or to waist level, it is advised that the weight limit should be within 15–25 kilograms for a secure and compact object that is being held close to the body and 15 kilograms for an object that is larger, bulkier or lifted further from the body.

When lifting from the floor or waist level to head height, the weight guideline is between 5 and 10 kilogrammes.

These weights may seem relatively light compared to the kind of weights we lift regularly, which simply highlights the kind of risks to which we subject ourselves every day when we exceed the manual handling safety guidelines.

Discussion: Errors in Lifting

Trainer's notes

Outline	
Format:	*Pairs/small groups*
Type:	*Discussion/problem solver*
Time:	*15 minutes, plus discussion*
Resources:	*Handout provided*

Objective

To identify situations from the delegates' own experience.

Procedure

Ask the delegates to look at the handout provided which identifies errors in lifting in everyday life and work situations. Tell them that these ten errors will result in nearly all manual handling or back-related injuries and disabilities. Ask them to review the list and rank them in order of importance.

After 15 minutes, discuss the ranking and any further errors identified.

📄 Discussion: Errors in Lifting

The following is a list of the top ten lifting errors identified from our everyday lives and work situations. Rank each in order of danger and try to add another ten errors to the list.

Lifting Error	Rank
Holding the load away from you	
Twisting	
Stooping	
Reaching upwards	
Excessive up and down movements	
Carrying over long distances	
Strenuous pushing or pulling	
Unpredictable or unbalanced loads	
Repetitive handling and lifting	
Work-rate too strenuous	

1.	
2.	
3.	
4.	
5.	
6.	
7.	
8.	
9.	
10.	

Brainteaser 1: Spot the Difference

Trainer's notes

Outline	
Format:	*Individual or pairs*
Type:	*Ice-breaker or session starter*
Time:	*5–10 minutes*
Resources:	*Handout provided*

Objective

To practise problem solving.

Procedure

Give delegates the handout provided and ask them to decide which, if any, are different and why.

Allow 3–5 minutes. Do not enter into any discussion.

After five minutes, ask delegates to share their ideas. See the answer section, for the solution.

Run a short discussion on the following points.

- How many of you gave up?

- How long did it take you to find a solution?

- What lessons might we learn about how to be more creative in our approach to problem solving?

📑 Brainteaser 1: Spot the Difference

Look at the four shapes below and see if you can find any difference.

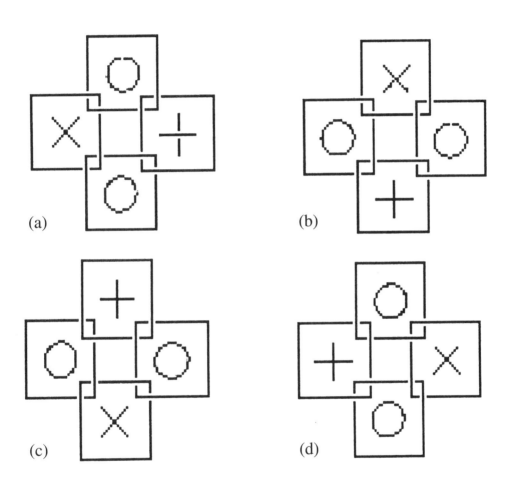

(a)

(b)

(c)

(d)

Reproduced from *Health and Safety Games for Trainers*, Graham Roberts-Phelps, Gower, Aldershot

Brainteaser 2: Nine Dots

Trainer's notes

<table>
<tr><td>Outline</td><td></td></tr>
<tr><td>Format:</td><td>Pairs or individuals</td></tr>
<tr><td>Type:</td><td>Ice-breaker or problem solving</td></tr>
<tr><td>Time:</td><td>10–15 minutes, plus discussion</td></tr>
<tr><td>Resources:</td><td>Handout provided, flip chart</td></tr>
</table>

Objective

To demonstrate how we constrain our thinking; that is our lack of ability to find solutions to problems because of our self-imposed assumptions.

Procedure

This puzzle is a classic and regular course-goers will usually have encountered it before, however those that have, often forget!

Ask the pairs or individuals to connect all nine dots using only four straight lines, without taking their pen off the paper.

Avoid entering any discussion as to methods – simply repeat the instructions.

After ten minutes, invite any successful delegate to draw the solution on the flip chart. See the answer section for the solution.

Run a short discussion on the following points.

- How many of you gave up after only a few minutes?

- How many of you tried to re-write or 'bend' the rules?

- Why did it seem relatively obvious once the solution had been discovered or displayed?

- What can this exercise tell us about our own approach to problem-solving and changing our methods of doing things?

▤ **Brainteaser 2: Nine Dots**

Connect the nine dots below using only four straight lines, without taking your pen off the paper.

Brainteaser 3: The Dream

Trainer's notes

Outline	
Format:	*Pairs or individuals*
Type:	*Ice-breaker or energizer*
Time:	*10–15 minutes, plus discussion*
Resources:	*Handout provided*

Objective

To practise creative and lateral thinking.

Procedure

Distribute the handout to pairs or individuals, or read it aloud.

Note: As an alternative format, delegates can work on the problem in larger groups, creating more of a group interaction and team-building exercise.

Whilst working on the puzzle, you can answer their questions with short yes or no answers, but be careful not to lead delegates too quickly to the answer. Encourage them to explore all possible options, thinking as laterally and creatively as possible.

The clues include the following.

Q. Was the man fired because he had had anything to do with the planting of the bomb?

A. No.

Q. Did the man genuinely dream about the bomb?

A. Yes.

Q. Did the boss have some kind of grudge against the man?

A. No.

Q. Were the man's particular responsibilities relevant?

A. Yes.

After 10–15 minutes ask the delegates for their responses or conclusions. See the answer section for the solution.

📄 Brainteaser 3: The Dream

The boss of a storage warehouse had just arrived at work when one of his employees burst into his office.

The man explained that while asleep the previous night he had dreamed that one of the stored boxes contained a bomb that would explode at two p.m., causing a terrible fire.

The boss was sceptical, but agreed to investigate. After a search, a bomb was found in the area foreseen in the man's dream. The police were called, the bomb defused, and a tragedy averted. Afterwards, the boss thanked the employee sincerely. Then he fired him.

The sacked man had not planted the bomb, and his prophetic dream had saved the warehouse from destruction. Yet the manager was right to fire him.

How could this be so?

Reproduced from *Health and Safety Games for Trainers*, Graham Roberts-Phelps, Gower, Aldershot

Brainteaser 4: World War I

Trainer's notes

> **Outline**
> **Format:** *Pairs or individuals*
> **Type:** *Ice-breaker or energizer*
> **Time:** *10–15 minutes, plus discussion*
> **Resources:** *Handout provided*

Objective

To practise creative and lateral thinking.

Procedure

Distribute the handout to pairs or individuals, or read it aloud.

As an alternative format, delegates can work on the problem in larger groups, creating more of a group interaction and team-building exercise.

Whilst working on the puzzle, you can answer their questions with short yes or no answers, but be careful not to lead delegates too quickly to the answer. Encourage delegates to explore all possible options, thinking as laterally and creatively as possible.

The clues include the following.

> Q: Did the men wear the helmets?
>
> A: Yes.
>
> Q: When they wore the helmets, did the incidence of head injuries increase?
>
> A: Yes.
>
> Q: And yet they were retained?
>
> A: Yes.
>
> Q: Were they beneficial?
>
> A: Yes.

After 10–15 minutes ask the delegates for their responses or conclusions. See the answer section for the solution.

📄 Brainteaser 4: World War I

At the beginning of World War I, the uniform of the British soldiers included a brown cloth cap. They were not provided with metal helmets.

As the war went on, the army authorities and the War Office became alarmed at the high proportion of men with head injuries. Therefore, they decided to replace all cloth headgear with metal helmets. From then on, all the soldiers wore the metal helmets.

However, the War Office was amazed to discover that the incidence of head injuries increased.

It can be assumed that the intensity of fighting was the same before and after the change. So why should the recorded number of head injuries per battalion increase when the men wore metal helmets instead of cloth caps.

Reproduced from *Health and Safety Games for Trainers*, Graham Roberts-Phelps, Gower, Aldershot

7.   Group Energizers

Accident Log
   Trainer's Notes
   Handout

Cricket Practice (Hazards and Risk Reduction)
   Trainer's Notes

Quizzes 1 and 2 Road Safety
   Trainer's Notes
   Handout 1
   Handout 2

Putting a Price on It
   Trainer's Notes
   Handout

Running Blind
   Trainer's Notes

Safety Dilemmas
   Trainer's Notes
   Handout

Safety Poster
   Trainer's Notes

Safety Awareness Bingo Quiz
   Trainer's Notes
   Handout

Safety Case Study
   Trainer's Notes
   Handout

Overcoming Obstacles to Safer Working
   Trainer's Notes

Quiz Challenge
    Trainer's Notes

Safety Best Practice
    Trainer's Notes
    Handout

Reasons to Learn
    Trainer's Notes

Safety Hazards and Risks
    Trainer's Notes

What Causes Workplace Accidents?
    Trainer's Notes

How Safe is your Job?
    Trainer's Notes

Checklist 1 and 2
    Trainer's Notes
    Handout 1 (Workplace Safety)
    Handout 2 (Workplace Safety)

Accident Log

Trainer's notes

Outline	
Format:	**Small groups or pairs**
Type:	**Introductory**
Time:	**10–15 minutes, plus discussion**
Resources:	**Handout provided, flip chart**

Objective

The purpose of this exercise is to introduce the subject of health and safety in general. It will highlight the fact that whereas everyone thinks that accidents always happen to other people, they can actually happen to us and to others around us.

Procedure

Start by stating that in reality, no matter how safe we think we are, there are always plenty of potential hazards and accidents around us.

For example, every weekend there are 2 000 DIY accidents in the home that require hospital treatment!

Therefore, we need to examine and analyse what kind of accidents, or 'near-misses' have happened to us in the past, either at work or at home. This may help us to prevent similar things occurring in the future.

After checking that delegates are clear on the instructions, perhaps offering an example of your own, distribute the handouts.

After 10–15 minutes, ask each pair or group to summarize their responses and points.

List any conclusions on common accidents and preventative measures on the flip chart, and lead delegates in a discussion of the advantages and disadvantages of different ways of reducing risk.

Discussion points include the following.

- What is the most common form of injury?
  (Note: Probably back-related or cuts/bruises.)

- What causes these?

- How could we/you prevent them?

- Do some 'injuries' take years to show themselves?
  (For example strains and hearing loss.)

📄 Accident Log

Make a list of all accidents, injuries, near-misses and other aches, pains and conditions that you have encountered or experienced, either at work or home.

 Reproduced from *Health and Safety Games for Trainers*, Graham Roberts-Phelps, Gower, Aldershot

Cricket Practice (Hazards and Risk Reduction)

Trainer's notes

```
Outline
Format:      Group
Type:        Warm up or summary game
Time:        10–15 minutes
Resources:   Soft ball
```

Objective

To test delegates' ability to think on their feet and their awareness of common hazards and risks. Not only does this activity liven up almost any training course, it is a very effective method of recalling and remembering key points.

Procedure

Explain that you will throw a soft ball to someone which they must catch (or retrieve), and then immediately think of a *specific* workplace hazard or danger (e.g. working on a ladder or unloading a lorry).

That person then throws the ball back to you as he or she says it.

You then throw it to another delegate who must catch it and shout out one idea for reducing the risks associated with that hazard (e.g. securing the foot of the ladder or using scaffolding or a mechanical hoist).

That person then throws the ball back to you.

If he or she cannot think of an idea, then the ball should be thrown back to you.

As you throw the ball, shout alternatively 'Hazard' and then 'Reduce risk'.

Repeat the exercise until most delegates have had at least two or three catches. Any delegate who takes more than ten seconds to answer is 'timed-out' and has to throw the ball back.

Difficulty can be increased by ensuring a fast pace, and of course as the more obvious hazards and risk reduction ideas are used up.

Quizzes 1 and 2: Road Safety

Trainer's notes

Outline	
Format:	*Individuals*
Type:	*Quiz*
Time:	*15 minutes, plus discussion*
Resources:	*Handout provided*

Objective

This is a good activity for introducing road safety as a topic or as a summary exercise. It can also be used as an ice-breaker or warm-up exercise.

Procedure

Distribute the handouts or replace the standard quiz with your own specific set of questions (be sure to adjust the time accordingly).

After 15 minutes, ask the delegates to swap papers and to mark each other's.

Review each question in turn, discussing fully any issues that arise.

Consider awarding a small prize to those with highest marks, if not, a round of applause will suffice.

📄 Quiz 1: Road Safety

1. *You should **only** use a hand-held telephone:*

    (a) If your car has an automatic gear change
    (b) If you need to make an emergency call
    (c) When you have stopped at a safe place
    (d) When travelling on a minor road

2. *What is the shortest overall stopping distance on a dry road with good brakes and tyres from 60 mph?*

    (a) 53 metres (175 feet)
    (b) 73 metres (240 feet)
    (c) 58 metres (190 feet)
    (d) 96 metres (315 feet)

3. *You are braking on a wet road. Your vehicle begins to skid. What is the first thing you should do?*

    (a) Release the brake fully
    (b) Quickly pull up the handbrake
    (c) Push harder on the brake pedal
    (d) Put your foot on the clutch

4. *You are on a good dry road surface and in a vehicle with good brakes and tyres. What is the shortest overall stopping distance at 40 mph?*

    (a) 23 metres (75 feet)
    (b) 96 metres (315 feet)
    (c) 36 metres (120 feet)
    (d) 53 metres (175 feet)

5. *How can you avoid wheel spin when driving in freezing conditions?*

    (a) Stay in first gear
    (b) Put your handbrake on if the wheel begins to slip
    (c) Drive in as high a gear as possible as slowly as possible
    (d) Allow the vehicle to coast in neutral

6. *The braking distance on ice can be:*

    (a) twice the normal distance
    (b) five times the normal distance
    (c) seven times the normal distance
    (d) ten times the normal distance

7. *You are turning left on a slippery road. The back of your vehicle slides to the right. What should you do?*

    (a) Break firmly and do not turn the steering wheel
    (b) Steer carefully to the right
    (c) Use the clutch and brake firmly
    (d) Turn only to the left

Reproduced from *Health and Safety Games for Trainers*, Graham Roberts-Phelps, Gower, Aldershot

8. *You are driving on an icy road. How can you avoid wheel spin?*

(a) Use the handbrake if the wheel starts to slip
(b) Drive at a slow speed in as high a gear as possible
(c) Brake gently and repeatedly
(d) Drive in a low gear at all times

9. *What is the braking distance at 50 mph in normal conditions?*

(a) 38 metres (125 feet)
(b) 55 metres (180 feet)
(c) 24 metres (79 feet)
(d) 14 metres (46 feet)

10. *What is the shortest stopping distance at 70 mph in normal conditions?*

(a) 53 metres (175 feet)
(b) 60 metres (200 feet)
(c) 96 metres (315 feet)
(d) 73 metres (240 feet)

11. *Which two of the following types of vehicles should you allow extra room for when overtaking?*

(a) Tractors
(b) Motorcycles
(c) Road-sweeping vehicles
(d) Bicycles

12. *You are following a vehicle on a wet road. You should leave a time gap of at least:*

(a) four seconds
(b) one second
(c) two seconds
(d) three seconds

13. *You are travelling on a fast road (with a speed limit of at least 60–70 mph) in good conditions. To be sure that you are at a safe distance:*

(a) The distance between you and the car in front should be twice the length of the vehicle
(b) The distance between you and the car in front should be your braking distance
(c) There should be a two-second time gap between you and the car in front
(d) There should be a one-second gap between you and the car in front

14. *You are driving in traffic at the speed limit for the road. The driver behind is trying to overtake. You should:*

(a) Move closer to the car ahead, so the driver behind has no room to overtake
(b) Wave the driver behind to overtake when it is safe
(c) Accelerate to get away from the driver behind
(d) Keep a steady course and allow the driver behind to overtake

Reproduced from *Health and Safety Games for Trainers*, Graham Roberts-Phelps, Gower, Aldershot

15. *A vehicle pulls out in front of you unexpectedly at a junction. What should you do?*

   (a) Swerve past it and blow your horn
   (b) Slow down and be ready to stop
   (c) Flash your headlights and drive close up behind
   (d) Accelerate past it immediately

📄 Quiz 2: Road Safety

1. *You should **only** flash you head lamps to other road users:*

   (a) To let them know you are there
   (b) To show you are giving way
   (c) To show you are about to reverse
   (d) To tell them you have right of way

2. *Which **two** of the following are causes of rear-end collisions?*

   (a) Driving too close to the vehicle in front
   (b) Traffic lights changing suddenly
   (c) Pedestrians crossing the road in busy built-up areas
   (d) Drivers not paying enough attention to the road
   (e) Stopping at every junction

3. *When driving, what is the maximum legal level for alcohol in the blood?*

   (a) 50mg per 100ml
   (b) 60mg per 100ml
   (c) 80mg per 100ml
   (d) 90mg per 100ml

4. *You should switch your rear fog light on when visibility drops below:*

   (a) Your overall stopping distance
   (b) ten car lengths
   (c) 10 metres
   (d) 100 metres

5. *How can you best control your vehicle when driving in snow?*

   (a) By staying in a low gear and gripping the steering wheel
   (b) By driving in first gear
   (c) By keeping the engine revs high and slipping the clutch
   (d) By driving slowly in as high a gear as possible

6. *You are travelling on a motorway at night with other vehicles ahead of you. Which lights should you have on?*

   (a) Front fog lights
   (b) Main beam headlights
   (c) Dipped headlights
   (d) Side lights only

7. *You are travelling on a motorway. What colour are the reflective studs on the left of the carriage way?*

   (a) Red
   (b) Green
   (c) White
   (d) Amber

 Reproduced from *Health and Safety Games for Trainers*, Graham Roberts-Phelps, Gower, Aldershot

8. *You get a puncture on the motorway. You manage to get your vehicle onto the hard shoulder. You should:*

    (a) Use the emergency telephone and call for assistance
    (b) Change the wheel yourself immediately
    (c) Try to wave down another vehicle for help
    (d) Only change the wheel if you have a passenger to help you

9. *In which three of the following situations may you stop on a motorway?*

    (a) If you have to read a map
    (b) If you are tired and need a rest
    (c) If red lights show above a lane
    (d) When told to by police
    (e) If a child in the car feels ill
    (f) In an emergency or a breakdown

10. *You are towing a trailer on a motorway. What is your maximum speed limit?*

    (a) 40mph (64kph)
    (b) 50mph (80kph)
    (c) 60mph (97kph)
    (d) 70mph (113kph)

11. *You are on a road which is only wide enough for one vehicle. There is a car coming towards you. Which **two** of these would be correct?*

    (a) Pull into a passing place on your right
    (b) Force the other driver to reverse
    (c) Pull into a passing place if your vehicle is wider
    (d) Pull into a passing place on your left
    (e) Wait opposite a passing place on your left
    (f) Wait opposite a passing place on your right

12. *You are parked in a busy high street. What is the safest way to turn your vehicle around?*

    (a) Drive into a side road and reverse onto the main road
    (b) Get someone to stop the traffic
    (c) Find a quiet side road in which to turn around
    (d) Do a U-turn

13. *Where you see street lights but no speed limit signs, the limit is usually:*

    (a) 30mph (48kph)
    (b) 40mph (64kph)
    (c) 50mph (80kph)
    (d) 60mph (97kph)

14. *You are on a busy main road and you find you are travelling in the wrong direction. What should you do?*

    (a) Turn into a side road on the right and reverse onto the main road
    (b) Turn around in a quiet side road
    (c) Make a U-turn in the main road
    (d) Make a 'three point' turn in the main road

15. *At a crossroads, there are no signs or road markings. Two vehicles approach, which has priority?*

(a) The vehicle travelling the fastest
(b) The vehicle on the widest road
(c) Vehicles approaching from the right
(d) Neither vehicle

 Reproduced from *Health and Safety Games for Trainers*, Graham Roberts-Phelps, Gower, Aldershot

Putting a Price on It

Trainer's notes

Outline	
Format:	*Small groups or pairs*
Type:	*Energizer/session starter*
Time:	*15–20 minutes, plus discussion*
Resources:	*Handout provided, flip chart*

Objective

To highlight the importance of health and safety, in that no amount of money or compensation can ever be a replacement for our health, fitness and well-being.

Procedure

Give the delegates the handout provided and ask them to work through the instructions on the handout. The group members should all agree unanimously on the decisions reached.

After about 15 minutes, ask each group in turn to transfer their findings to a flip chart and present a brief summary of the group discussion.

You might like to add the 'right' answer at the end – the figures in the answer section are based on a typical rating from a personal accident insurance policy.

📄 Putting a Price on It

You have been asked by an insurance company to express your view as to what compensation you think that you should receive on the loss, or loss of use, of various parts of your body. Discuss and agree on a set of figures for compensation. Elect a spokesperson and be ready to present these to the group discussion which will follow.

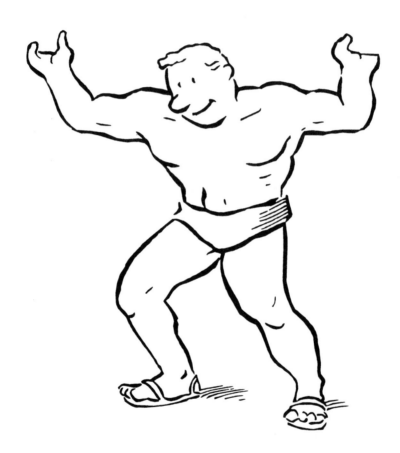

Reproduced from *Health and Safety Games for Trainers*, Graham Roberts-Phelps, Gower, Aldershot

Running Blind

Trainer's notes

Outline	
Format:	*Pairs or small groups*
Type:	*Warm-up game or ice-breaker*
Time:	*15–20 minutes, plus discussion*
Resources:	*Jugs of water, glasses, blindfolds, a large room with chairs and tables*

Objective

To reinforce how much we rely on sight. This is an excellent way of getting home the message that wearing eye protection and using safety guards are very good ideas and may be mandatory.

Procedure

In preparation, arrange the jugs of water and glasses at one end of the room. Scatter chairs, tables and obstacles around room.

Divide the group into pairs or small groups.

Explain that one person will be blindfolded, and the other person will act as that person's 'eyes', i.e. guiding him or her through the following exercise.

Direct delegates to the opposite end of the room to the water and glasses. Explain that the purpose of this exercise is to guide the blindfolded person safely past all the obstacles (hazards) in the room, to the jug of water. Then, still blindfolded, that person should fill a glass to the brim with water and make the return journey. The first person to make it back to the start, with the most water in the glass wins!

Lead a discussion, including the following points.

- How did it feel being unable to see?

- Did the other person give you good advice?

- Did rushing or hurrying help you or make you spill water?

- What does this exercise teach us?

Safety Dilemmas

Trainer's notes

Outline	
Format:	*Individuals*
Type:	*Quiz*
Time:	*15–20 minutes, plus discussion*
Resources:	*Handout provided, flip chart*

Objective

This activity gets delegates thinking about everyday safety issues and their consequences.

Procedure

Give delegates the handouts provided. Allow 15 minutes for them to complete the quiz.

You might want to supplement or replace the standard quiz with your own specific set of questions. Be sure to adjust the time accordingly.

After the time is up, ask delegates to swap papers and to mark each other's.

Review each question in turn, discussing fully any issues that arise. Summarize the key points on a flip chart.

📄 Safety Dilemmas

Consider each of the following questions carefully and mark each with a ✓ as yes or no and then detail what you would do in each case.

Question	Yes	No
1. You cut your hand on a staple when unpacking a box. You wrap your handkerchief around it and it soon stops bleeding. Do you report it as an accident?		
2. You notice that several of your colleagues or staff do not wear their ear protection in the plant as they are supposed. Do you say anything to them, or do you bring this to the attention of your supervisor?		
3. The fire alarm rings while you are in the middle of a complicated job and it is still ringing after 15 or 20 seconds. You feel sure it is a false alarm although you were not told of a fire drill being scheduled (which is usually the case). Do you keep working a bit longer and see if it stops in a minute?		
4. As you leave work one afternoon, you notice somebody hanging around the car park whom you do not recognize. This person is looking a bit suspicious, do you approach him or her to ask what he or she is doing?		

Safety Poster

Trainer's notes

```
Outline
Format:      Groups
Type:        Energizer
Time:        20–30 minutes
Resources:   Flip chart/s
```

Objective

To guide delegates in identifying key behaviours and characteristics of good safety behaviours.

Procedure

This exercise gets everybody up, talking and moving around the room. It is also impossible to take too seriously, although the content of the discussion and posters reinforces some key attributes needed for good safety practice.

Introduce the exercise by asking delegates to recall health and safety posters.

Tell them that in this exercise they will have a chance to design their own.

Divide delegates into groups of two or three and hand them several sheets of flip-chart paper.

Tell them they have to design a 'Safety Poster' on one aspect of good safety practice.

The poster should describe what behaviour or standards to follow, or motivate or remind people to follow such practice. It may also draw attention to the consequences of not following good safety practice.

Allow about 20 minutes. Then pin the posters around the room and refer to them as you draw attention to key points raised during the training course.

Safety Awareness Bingo Quiz

Trainer's notes

> **Outline**
> **Format:** *Individuals*
> **Type:** *Ice-breaker*
> **Time:** *15–20 minutes, plus discussion*
> **Resources:** *Handout provided, small prizes*

Objective

To highlight the importance of safety.

Procedure

Give the delegates the handout provided and ask them to choose nine numbers between 1 and 25 and to write them in the boxes on the grid. (This ensures a random element to the game.)

Next, *select at random* and read out the following questions one at a time, making sure that if the delegates have a box with the corresponding number, they write the answer in that box.

You can read out the number of the question 'bingo' style, e.g. 'garden gate – number eight'. You could also add your own questions.

Delegates should raise their hand when they have a line.

Whenever somebody has a line, stop and check that their answers are correct. The line is **only** valid if all the answers are correct.

Reward each line winner with a small prize.

Continue until a full house is called, and again check the answers first. The full house is **only** valid if all the answers are correct. If they are not, continue.

The game ends when a full house is achieved by a delegate, or when all questions have been read out.

At the end of the game read the questions and the answers so that delegates can check their answers.

Question	Answer
1. Large organizations (50 or more employees) have a worse safety record than small ones. True or false?	*False*
2. How often should safety assessments/inspections be carried out?	*Every 12 months*
3. Which regulations cover the wearing of ear and eye protection?	*PPE*
4. What is the number of decibels over which ear protection must be worn?	*90*

Question	Answer
5. You, as employees, are legally bound to do this.	*Follow safety rules*
6. A Safety Inspector has right of entry. True or False?	*True*
7. What is the main legislation that covers all workplaces?	*Health and Safety at Work Act (1974)*
8. What is the most common way that accident/injury occurs?	*Manual handling*
9. What is the second most common way that accident/injury occurs?	*Slips and trips*
10. List three negative attitudes that contribute to accidents.	*Laziness, not following instructions, showing-off*
11. Name a common disease affecting the skin.	*Dermatitis*
12. What is the average amount of time off work for a back injury?	*Four weeks*
13. What problem can be caused by repetitive and light lifting or movement.	*RSI*
14. Once provided, you legally have to wear protective equipment. True or False?	*True*
15. What does a safety sign with a yellow background and black writing signify?	*A warning – care and caution instruction*
16. What do you understand by the term RSI?	*Repetitive strain injury*
17. What would you do if your computer started making an unusual noise?	*Turn it off and call a qualified engineer*
18. When using a keyboard, in what position should your forearms and elbows be?	*Level*
19. What is the best distance to sit away from your screen?	*18 inches*
20. Your employer is obliged to pay for an eye test and glasses if you request them. True or False?	*False*

Question	Answer
21. What does a safety sign with a blue background and white writing signify?	A 'must do' instruction
22. How many accidents occur at work every year?	1 600 000
23. How many people are killed at work every year?	600
24. What does HASAWA stand for?	Health and Safety at Work Act (1974)
25. What are the regulations covering hazardous chemicals?	COSHH

📄 Safety Bingo Quiz

Please choose nine numbers between 1 and 25 and place them anywhere in the grid.

You will hear one question at a time. If you have that number question, please write the answer in that numbered square.

*You should raise your hand when you have line or a full house. The line or full house is **only** valid if all the answers are correct.*

Reproduced from *Health and Safety Games for Trainers*, Graham Roberts-Phelps, Gower, Aldershot

Safety Case Study

Trainer's notes

Outline
Format:	*Pairs/small groups*
Type:	*Discussion/problem solver*
Time:	*15 minutes, plus discussion*
Resources:	*Handout provided*

Objective

To highlight some of the causes and factors that can contribute to accidents at work and the need for greater personal responsibility.

Procedure

Give the delegates the handout provided. Ask them to read the case study and to decide on the advice that they would give to Dave.

After 15 minutes, gather responses and discuss.

📄 Safety Case Study

Read the following case study. Then, in pairs or a small group, work out what advice you would give Dave.

'Jim Walker was one of those people you couldn't help but like. Nothing was ever too much trouble and he never had a bad word to say about anything. This made the task of Dave, his Foreman, even harder.

Dave was concerned about Jim's lack of attention when it came to safety. He frequently and plainly disregarded instructions when it came to the wearing of safety equipment. For instance, he only wore safety gloves when his hands got cold and refused to wear the safety boots when it was too hot. The company had invested a lot more time and money over the previous 12 months in new safety guards, protective equipment and notices, and yet the place didn't seem to be much safer for it.

Jim's pranks regarding using the warehouse loading bay for cricket practice also nearly got him, and everybody else, in hot water. A French juggernaut unexpectedly swung round the corner and it was only the air-brakes and the driver's quick reactions that avoided a nasty accident. The driver was furious – made even worse as the driver didn't know what cricket was!

However, Dave had now begun to notice that several other of the other younger men had picked up Jim's bad habits. Goggles, shoes and other protective equipment were not being worn and sloppy behaviour was beginning to creep in. For instance, the warehouse was a mess with boxes left in gangways and packing areas not properly laid out.

Dave knew that if he didn't do something soon, then it would only be a matter of time before there was an accident or injury. He had tried talking to Jim about it, and Jim had listened and promised to be more careful, but nothing changed, at least not for more than a few days.

Dave was at a loss what to do. Should he get tough with Jim and risk upsetting him, and probably everybody else. Or should he get tough with everybody in the hope that Jim would toe the line? In what other way could he solve the problem other than through confrontation?'

Reproduced from *Health and Safety Games for Trainers*, Graham Roberts-Phelps, Gower, Aldershot

Overcoming Obstacles to Safer Working

Trainer's notes

Outline	
Format:	**Pairs or small groups**
Type:	**Discussion/problem solver**
Time:	**10 minutes, plus discussion**
Resources:	**Paper**

Objective

To raise and, hopefully, overcome problems or issues regarding implementing safety practices and standards.

Procedure

Ask the delegates to discuss and agree on what might be the most frequent obstacle or difficulty in maintaining workplace safety standards or putting into practice any of the ideas from this training session.

Each group/pair should write this problem on a sheet of paper then pass it to another group, collecting one of that group's obstacles in return.

Within the group/pair there should follow a discussion of ways of overcoming these obstacles.

After 10 minutes, groups/pairs should present their ideas and solutions to the whole group.

Quiz Challenge

Trainer's notes

Outline	
Format:	Groups
Type:	Quiz
Time:	30 minutes
Resources:	Paper

Objective

An alternative way of ending a training session that serves to review key learning points.

Procedure

Ask the groups of delegates to develop six questions to test the other teams. These questions should be based on information covered during the course.

After 15 minutes they should nominate a spokesperson to deliver the questions.

This same person should answer the questions from the other groups.

Safety Best Practice

Trainer's notes

Outline	
Format:	*Pairs/small groups*
Type:	*Discussion/improvement planner*
Time:	*15 minutes, plus discussion*
Resources:	*Handout provided*

Objective

To establish, reinforce or clarify safety standards and working practice.

Procedure

Give the delegates the handout provided. Ask them to prepare a list of dos and don'ts as advice regarding safety awareness and ways of reducing risks in the workplace.

After 15 minutes, gather responses and discuss.

📄 Safety Best Practice

What advice would you give to somebody regarding safety awareness and ways of reducing risks in the workplace?

'Do'	'Don't'

Reproduced from *Health and Safety Games for Trainers*, Graham Roberts-Phelps, Gower, Aldershot

Reasons to Learn

Trainer's notes

Outline
Format: **Pairs/small groups**
Type: **Discussion/session starter**
Time: **10 minutes, plus discussion**
Resources: **Paper**

Objective

To highlight the importance of health and safety.

Procedure

Ask delegates the following two questions.

- What benefits or advantages derive when people are more health and safety conscious and skilled?

- What difficulties or disadvantages arise when people are not very aware of good workplace safety methods and practices?

Ask them to list their responses under the headings 'benefits of good workplace safety' and 'disadvantages of poor workplace safety'. After 10 minutes, gather responses and discuss.

Safety Hazards and Risks

Trainer's notes

Outline	
Format:	*Small groups*
Type:	*Discussion*
Time:	*10 minutes, plus discussion*
Resources:	*Paper*

Objective

To clarify two very important health and safety terms.

Procedure

Ask the delegates to answer the following two questions

- What is the difference between a hazard and a risk?

- What hazards and risks exist in your workplace?

In answering the second question delegates should be specific and give examples. They should consider not only their experience in their present jobs, but in previous ones too.

After 10 minutes, gather responses and discuss.

What Causes Workplace Accidents?

Trainer's notes

Outline	
Format:	*Small groups*
Type:	*Discussion*
Time:	*10 minutes, plus discussion*
Resources:	*Paper*

Objective

To identify the cause and effect relationship between accidents, ill-health and near misses.

Procedure

Ask the delegates to answer the following question

- Have there been any accidents, injuries or 'near misses' in your workplace (or in your experience)? If so, what do you think might have caused them or been contributing factors?

Delegates should consider not only their experience in their present jobs, but in previous ones too.

After 10 minutes, gather responses and discuss.

How Safe is Your Job?

Trainer's notes

Outline	
Format:	*Small groups*
Type:	*Discussion*
Time:	*10 minutes, plus discussion*
Resources:	*Paper*

Objective

To recognize and identify the hazards and risks that exist in delegates' jobs/work. The aim is to highlight that every job has both hazards and risks that can increase or decrease, based on the individual's safety knowledge and attitude.

Procedure

Ask the delegates to answer the following question

- Do you think that working in your job, environment or workplace presents more or fewer health and safety hazards than other types of job or working environment? List examples.

Delegates should consider not only their experience in their present jobs, but in previous ones too.

After 10 minutes, gather responses and discuss.

Checklist 1 and 2

Trainer's notes

Outline	
Format:	*Small groups*
Type:	*Discussion*
Time:	*10 minutes, plus discussion*
Resources:	*Handout provided*

Objective

To identify and perhaps formalize elements of safe working practice.

Procedure

Distribute the handouts and ask delegates to work through the checklists. After 10 minutes, gather responses and discuss.

📄 Checklist 1: Workplace Safety

Make a list of some of the things that you might consider when assessing your workplace environment. You might find it useful to make a list under each of these four categories.

1. Plant and equipment	2. Tasks and procedures
3. The work environment, including plant and equipment	4. People

Reproduced from *Health and Safety Games for Trainers*, Graham Roberts-Phelps, Gower, Aldershot

Checklist 2: Workplace Safety

Make a list of 10 things that you believe might reduce or remove the risk of injury, accident or discomfort when working in your normal place of work.

These might involve your work area, individuals, managers, your company or organization, suppliers or customers.

Ways of reducing the risk of injury, accident or discomfort
1.
2.
3.
4.
5.
6.
7.
8.
9.
10.

8. Safety Case Studies and Legislation Discussion Groups

Activities 1–4 Risk Assessment
  Trainer's Notes
  Handout 1
  Handout 2
  Handout 3
  Handout 4

101 Ideas for a Safer Business
  Trainer's Notes
  Handout

Acts and Regulations
  Trainer's Notes
  The Health and Safety at Work Act 1974 Handout
  The Electricity at Work Regulations 1989 Handout
  The COSHH Regulations 1988 Handout
  The Manual Handling Regulations 1992 Handout
  The Noise at Work Regulations 1989 Handout
  The Fire Precautions Act 1971 Handout
  The Display Screen Equipment Regulations 1992 Handout
  The Workplace Regulations (Heath, Safety and Welfare) 1992 Handout
  The Management of Health and Safety at Work Regulations 1992 Handout

Discussion Groups 1 and 2
  Trainer's Notes
  Handout 1 (Safety Awareness)
  Handout 2 (Hazards and Risks)

Case Study: Accident Report
  Trainer's Notes
  Handout

Problems, Causes and Solutions
  Trainer's Notes
  Handout

Activities 1–4 Risk Assessment

Trainer's notes

Outline	
Format:	*Pairs/small groups*
Type:	*Discussion*
Time:	*10 minutes, plus discussion*
Resources:	*Handout provided*

Objective

To familiarize delegates with elements and strategies involved in completing risk-assessment.

Procedure

Give the first handout to the delegates.

After 10 minutes, gather responses and discuss.

Repeat with handouts 2, 3 and 4 and follow each with a discussion.

📄 Activity 1: Risk Assessment

Make a list of some of the jobs, tasks and operations that you or other people perform. For each one identify as many hazards as you can.

Job, task or operation	Hazards

Reproduced from *Health and Safety Games for Trainers*, Graham Roberts-Phelps, Gower, Aldershot

📄 Activity 2: Risk Assessment

Think again about the other people in your workplace. They may be those you listed in Activity 1 or others who are not in the workplace all the time, e.g. cleaners, visitors, contractors and maintenance personnel.

These people will include members of the public if there is a chance they could be hurt by your activities.

You have a responsibility under the law to safeguard anybody who might be affected by what you do.

List here how the safety of those people might be better safeguarded.

People	Ways to protect them against risk

📄 Activity 3: Risk Assessment

List the hazards you wrote down in Activity 1 and rate each one on a scale of 1 to 5 for degree of harm that may be caused, and A to E for the chance of that harm happening, that is the risk.

Hazard rating: on a scale of 1 to 5

Score 5 as the highest and 1 as lowest. For example, a cleaning process that produces toxic fumes would be 4 or 5. Increase the hazard rating if a number of people may be involved or affected.

Risk rating: A to E for potential to cause harm

Score A as the highest and E as lowest. An 'A' category risk would be one with a very high (80 per cent or more) chance of happening, and an 'E' category risk would be one with little (10 per cent or less) chance of happening. An example of a low risk would be using an electric drill – whilst it can kill, the chances (or 'risk') of that happening in an office where everything is properly installed and earthed is small.

Hazard	Hazard rating (1–5)	Risk rating (A–E)

Reproduced from *Health and Safety Games for Trainers*, Graham Roberts-Phelps, Gower, Aldershot

📄 Activity 4: Risk Assessment

Based on the list of hazards you made in Activity 1, select the most significant hazards. Then review each one in turn and consider the following.

- *Could the hazard be removed or prevented altogether?*
- *What else could be done to reduce and control the risks associated with this hazard?*

Hazard	Steps to removing or reducing it

101 Ideas for a Safer Business

Trainer's notes

Objective

To review/identify practical ideas to further improve safety standards

Procedure

Give the handout provided to the delegates.

Ask them to discuss the list of safety facts and ideas within their groups. They should select the best or most relevant five ideas and add one more of their own.

After 30 minutes, gather responses, transfer the additional ideas on to a flip chart and discuss.

📄 101 Ideas for a Safer Business

Discuss the following list of safety facts and ideas within your group.

Select the best or most relevant five ideas and add one more of your own.

The Law and You

1. The Health and Safety at Work Act 1974 is the main law. It covers all work premises and everyone at work.

2. It says you must look after everyone working for you or on your premises, and anyone who could be affected by what you do – including the public.

3. There are other laws and regulations, and new ones coming mainly from Europe. Find out what applies to you by asking your trade association, chamber of commerce, local council or your local Health and Safety Executive (HSE).

4. The law is enforced by inspectors from the HSE or your local council.

5. Inspectors spend most of their time giving advice to help you get your safety approach right.

6. They have powers to visit your workplace without notice and you must cooperate with them. They can issue legal notices requiring improvements or stopping work on the spot against which you can appeal. They can even prosecute you. Getting it right through cooperation is by far the better way.

7. Most businesses must be registered with the HSE's or the local council's inspectors. You can phone them to find out which.

8. You must have employer's liability insurance and display your certificate. You must also display a poster giving information about health and safety law for your employees or give them a leaflet – you can get these from The Stationery Office.

9. Children under 16 years of age cannot generally be employed full time. Check for by-laws with your local authority.

10. Health and safety has to be managed. Get organized. If your business has five or more employees, you must have a written health and safety policy statement which says who is responsible for what. Make sure everyone gets training, so that they know what they have to do. Remember though that 'the buck stops with you'.

Safe Systems of Work

11. The law requires you to provide safe and healthy systems of work for the employees in your business.

12. One-quarter of fatal accidents are caused by, and the health of many workers damaged as a result of, safe systems of work not being provided or being ignored.

13. Not all jobs are hazardous, but if they are, there must be systems of work which reduce risks to a minimum.

Reproduced from *Health and Safety Games for Trainers*, Graham Roberts-Phelps, Gower, Aldershot

14. Some risks are very clear and are overcome, for instance, by guarding. There may be other risks which are not so obvious, e.g. from maintenance, cleaning, breakdowns, chemical releases or emergencies.

15. Look at every job, think about what is used, who does what, when, where and how it is done.

16. First, look for any hazards your workplace may have and weigh up the risks. Then get rid of the hazards if you can.

17. If you cannot get rid of the hazards, you will need to put together safe systems to deal with them. Plan each job carefully from the start, decide who is in charge and how people know when to start the job, what to do and in what order.

18. When you have done this, tell employees how the job must be done. Where the job is complex or risks are high, put instructions in writing. In some cases, you may need a written permit to work. Staff should be trained so that they know what to do and can do it.

19. Employees must be informed of what could go wrong if they do not follow the safe system, and what to do if things do go wrong. Make sure there is supervision.

20. Check that all employees, at every level, follow the safe system of work. Ask for employees' own ideas, as these might help to reduce the number of risky jobs and improve the way they are carried out.

The Workplace

---

21. There should be enough toilets for the staff. Keep them clean, well lit, ventilated and in good working order.

22. There should be enough hot and cold (or warm) running water, soap and towels (or an electric dryer).

23. A clearly marked supply of wholesome drinking water should be provided.

24. The temperature must be a minimum of 16°C (60°F) where people sit at their work. Where work involves physical effort, the temperature can be lower at 13°C (55°F), but not less than this.

25. Premises should be clean. Good housekeeping is important. Dirt and refuse must be removed regularly – daily in factories. Floors should be cleaned regularly – weekly in factories. Internal walls should also be kept clean.

26. Make sure there is enough natural or artificial light to make the workplace and the work activities safe and to avoid problems of visual fatigue.

27. Each person must have enough space in which to work. The layout of each work station (seats, benches, machinery, controls, etc.) must be suitable for any person working there, allow safe working and prevent injury from lifting or from repeated awkward movements or poor posture.

28. The premises must be effectively ventilated. Heating systems should not give off fumes into the workplace.

29. Clothing lockers or hanging space must be provided for work or home clothing. There should also be provision for the drying of wet clothes.

30. Floors should be kept clean, level, unbroken and non-slip. Gangways should be clear and unobstructed, and exits properly marked.

Machines

31. Machinery must be safe to use. This usually means guarding the dangerous parts. Some machinery or parts of machines, such as lifting tackle, cranes and air receivers, must be inspected regularly by a competent person – usually from an insurance company.

32. Operators should receive instruction and training. Do not allow untrained people to use machines.

33. Some things, such as abrasive wheels and woodworking machines, are covered by special regulations. These require special standards of guarding. Find out about them.

34. Check regularly that guards are in place and working properly.

35. Make sure controls are properly marked and cannot be operated by mistake. Use shrouded start buttons and pedals.

36. People using machines should not wear dangling chains, ties, belts, loose clothing, gloves or rings, or have long hair worn loose, that could get caught up in moving parts. Eye protection should be worn where necessary.

37. Check that emergency stops are brightly coloured and easily reached.

38. If guards have been removed for maintenance, check that they are then replaced and secured.

39. Never let machines be cleaned while they are in motion.

40. Do not let people defeat or get around guards or safety devices. This should be a disciplinary – or even a sackable – offence.

Health

41. Identify any health risks in your workplace, such as substances, noise, handling, infection, allergies, radiation or vibration, in order to help you decide how to prevent them. More people suffer from work-related ill health each year than from injuries.

42. Make a list of all the substances used in your workplace and how they are used. (Find out what actually happens, not what you think happens.) Read the labels on the containers. Obtain the health and safety data sheets from your suppliers (suppliers must provide them).

43. Look at how each substance is used, what the labels and data sheets say and decide on what precautions you need to take.

44. If possible, substitute any dangerous substance with a less harmful one. Separate people from substances by enclosing the process. Keep fumes or dust away from people by using local exhaust ventilation. Where less harmful substances can't be used, enclose the process or use ventilation systems, then protective equipment (goggles, gloves, aprons, boots, masks, etc.) must be provided.

45. Employees should be trained to take the right precautions. They should be monitored to check that they do.

46. Protective equipment (including ventilation) should be maintained and replaced when necessary.

47. Write down what you have done – keep records.

48. Air monitoring or health checks may be needed. Ask the inspector for advice.

49. Work stations, tools and equipment should be comfortable and suitable for the person working there. Adjustable seating may be needed. Remember that matching people's capabilities with particular jobs will help prevent back pain and arm, wrist and hand problems. Do not ask people to do jobs which are physically too demanding for them.

50. Drink, drugs and medicines can affect people's ability to work safely. Be on the lookout for this.

Transport and Handling

51. There should be someone in charge of transport safety at your workplace. As far as possible, keep people and vehicles apart. Mark out gangways and roadways and keep them clear. Have a speed limit.

52. Vehicle drivers – particularly lift-truck operators – must be properly trained. Don't let untrained people drive. Make sure drivers remove keys so that others cannot be tempted.

53. Check that vehicle movements – particularly reversing – are done safely. Have someone watching and guiding the driver, but not from directly behind the vehicle.

54. Take great care during maintenance, by applying the brakes, chocking the wheels and using proper jack/axle stands. Always use a tyre cage.

55. Reduce lifting/manual handling as much as possible. Provide handling aids, e.g. sack trucks, trolleys, hoists and conveyors.

56. Make sure people are trained in how to lift and handle things properly.

57. If there is a crane at your workplace, make sure only trained people operate it or act as slinger.

58. Never let anyone stand under a load or let a load be taken over people.

59. Use the right sling for the job. Never let sling angles be greater than 120 degrees – better not more than 90 degrees. Remember that the strain on the sling increases as the angle increases.

60. Don't let people climb racks to reach upper shelves. Instead, they should use properly fixed ladders or steps. Objects should not stick out from shelves or stacks into gangways.

Electricity

61. All electrical installations have to be inspected and tested periodically. This should be done by a competent electrician.

62. Keep a list of portable tools and appliances such as drills, kettles, fires and radios. Inspect them regularly and have them periodically tested by a competent electrician. Any repairs or maintenance must be carried out by someone with proper training or experience.

Reproduced from *Health and Safety Games for Trainers*, Graham Roberts-Phelps, Gower, Aldershot

63. Staff should be aware of what to do if someone gets an electric shock.

64. If enough socket outlets are provided, there is no need for long extension cables and multi-way adapters, which can be a fire hazard. If necessary, use a short extension lead with a multi-socket block.

65. Always use a proper plug. Check regularly that the terminals are tight and the cables firmly clamped. Always use the correct fuse.

66. Replace frayed or damaged cables completely. Where you need to join cables, use a proper cable connector not twisted joints or screw terminal blocks.

67. There must be a clearly marked switch near each fixed machine to cut off power in an emergency.

68. Power cables to machines should be armoured, covered in thick flexible rubber, PVC or installed in a conduit.

69. On machines which need to be earthed, the earth must be kept in good condition.

70. All outdoor sockets and electrical equipment used in corrosive or damp conditions (such as 'power washers') should be of special design and protected by a 30mA residual current circuit breaker. Get specialist advice.

Stopping Falls

71. Falls kill and injure many people at work. A person should be appointed to ensure that falls are prevented.

72. Ensure ladders are tied at the top, are long enough for the job and have a good footing. Make sure the slope is right (one in four).

73. Ensure staircases have proper handrails if there are more than three risers.

74. Read the instructions before building a tower scaffold. Do not make mobile scaffolds too high. Use them only on firm and level ground. Anchor them or fit outriggers. Have guardrails and toeboards all round. Provide a proper way of getting up – never climb the outside. Make sure brakes are on and locked when in use.

75. Fixed scaffolds must be put up (and taken down) only by competent and experienced people. They should be inspected by a competent person weekly.

76. Buildings with fragile roofs (asbestos, glass, etc.) should have a warning sign.

77. Do not let people on fragile roofs without making sure they know the precautionary use of crawling boards, guardrails, safety harnesses and proper means of access.

78. Do not use a fork lift truck as a makeshift high-level working platform.

79. Cover floor openings or put a fence round them. Fence floor edges.

80. To stop things falling on people below, use barriers and warning notices.

81. If you have to shout to be heard clearly from about two metres away, you probably have a noise problem.

82. Find out how serious it is with the help of a competent person. Your trade association or the HSE will help you find one.

83. Your competent person should tell you what to do, where to get help and what your legal duties are.

84. Act on their recommendations. Staff should be aware that too much noise will make them deaf.

85. Insist that your machinery suppliers tell you the noise levels of their machines at the operator's position. Buy quiet machines and choose quiet processes.

86. Put noisy machines and processes in separate rooms or enclose them with sound insulation (your competent person may help here). Mark the area as an ear-defender zone if it is still noisy.

87. Staff should be informed of what precautions to take and what their legal responsibilities are.

88. Ear defenders should be used as a last resort. People should be given a choice of ear protection, but make sure those supplied reduce noise to a safe level. Make sure people wear them.

89. Reduce the length of noise exposure by job rotation and/or providing 'noise refuges', namely places where people can get away from the noise.

90. Keep checking that your precautions are working.

Accidents and Emergencies

91. All injuries should be recorded in an accident book.

92. Some accidents, diseases and 'near misses' must be reported to your local inspector. If anyone is killed, has to go to hospital for 24 hours or more, or breaks an arm or leg, you must phone your inspector straight away, and send in a special form (F2508 available from The Stationery Office) within seven days. If anyone is injured or made ill so that they are off work for more than three days, you must send in the special form within seven days. If 'near misses' occur, such as collapses, explosions, major fires or electrical faults, you must also report them. Ask your inspector if you are unsure.

93. Investigate all accidents or 'near misses' to see how you can make sure they do not happen again.

94. Plan for things that might go wrong (such as explosions, fires, floods and electrocutions). If it can go wrong, it will. There should be someone in charge of emergencies.

95. Employees should be informed of what might happen, who will be in charge, what to do and where to go.

96. Make sure all access/escape routes are clear, and that important items such as shut off valves, electrical isolators and fire-fighting equipment are clearly labelled.

97. If you need to evacuate the building, make sure you have procedures for everyone – staff and visitors – to follow.

98. First aid can save lives. You must have enough trained first aiders to give cover at all times.

99. You must have a first aid box containing enough of the right materials. Put a list of first aiders' names on the box.

100. You must also display notices giving the name of your first aiders and where to find the first aid box.

101. **If you've done everything above, you've made a good start. But keep it up. Get advice when you need it; keep in touch with your trade association, your chamber of commerce and your inspector. Keep up to date and keep your business safe and sound.**

Acts and Regulations

Trainer's notes

> *Outline*
> *Format:* **Small groups**
> *Type:* **Discussion**
> *Time:* **20 minutes, plus discussion**
> *Resources:* **Handouts provided**

Objective

To give delegates a practical and brief summary of key legislation.

Procedure

Give the handouts provided. There is information on nine sets of legislation provided for you to choose from:

- the Health and Safety at Work Act 1974

- the Electricity at Work Regulations 1989

- the COSHH Regulations 1988

- the Manual Handling Regulations 1992

- the Noise at Work Regulations 1989

- the Fire Precautions Act 1971

- the Display Screen Equipment Regulations 1992

- the Workplace Regulations (Health, Safety and Welfare) 1992

- the Management of Health and Safety at Work Regulations 1992

After reading and discussing the safety legislation, the groups should prepare a short (3–5 minute) presentation, highlighting any areas that may need attention in their workplace. It might be useful to categorize under the headings 'attitudes', 'equipment', 'procedures' and 'skills'.

After 20 minutes, ask delegates to give their presentations and discuss.

The Health and Safety at Work Act 1974

Working in a small group, discuss the following safety legislation and produce a short (3–5 minute) presentation, highlighting any areas that may need attention in your workplace. Categorize your points under the headings 'Attitudes', 'Equipment', 'Procedures' and 'Skills'.

This is the main law that covers **everyone** at work and **all work premises**. This piece of legislation was enacted in 1974, as the name suggests. It was brought in to replace and update much of the old Health and Safety law that was contained in the Factories Act of 1961 and the Offices, Shops and Railway Premises Act of 1963. These two pieces of legislation were fast becoming out-of-date with modern working practices, technology and equipment.

Under the Health and Safety at Work Act, a company has to ensure the health and safety of all its employees. Individuals have to ensure the health and safety of themselves and others around them who may be affected by what they do or fail to do. This includes contractors, as well as customers or indeed anybody who may visit or come into contact with the organization.

Safety studies have highlighted that small firms (fewer than 50 employees) have worse accident records than large organizations. This is made even worse by the large number of accidents that go unreported by small companies. Ignorance, poor standards and contempt for basic safety standards have been highlighted as key contributors.

The Act applies to all work activities and premises and everyone at work, including self-employed people, has responsibilities under it. Here are some key points raised by the Act.

1. Safeguards

Employers are required to implement reasonable safeguards to ensure safe working practice at all times. This means taking every practical step to remove hazards and to reduce or eliminate risks.The law interprets this as taking every possible precaution, and cost is not considered as an excuse for failure to do this.

2. Written Policy

All organizations employing five or more people must have a written and up-to-date health and safety policy. They must also carry out written risk assessments as part of the implementation of their safety policy. They must also display a current certificate as required by the Employer's Liability Act 1880.

3. Training and Information

Following from this, all staff must be fully trained in the company's safety policy and procedures in order to carry out their normal work duties. This means displaying health and safety regulations, safety signs, as well as formally training and directing staff on all aspects of health, safety, hazards and risks.

The legislation does not just cover employers and organizations, there are also definite requirements placed on employees. All employees must take reasonable care, not only to protect themselves but also their colleagues. They are also required to follow all health and safety policy regulations and procedures, and to cooperate fully with health and safety representatives and officers in their job of implementing health and safety policy. Failure to do so is in breach of the Act.

'HSE inspectors can visit your premises without notice and gain right of entry. They have the power to stop your work, close premises and even prosecute.'

5. Safe Systems of Work

Employers must also ensure that there are what are known as 'safe systems of work'. This means creating an environment that is conducive to health and safety. This can be as basic as making sure that buildings are in good repair, that proper heat and ventilation are provided, and that the workplace is clean and hygienic to work in. It may also mean having clear procedures and checklists to make sure that safety is implemented. In some cases, it may require a permit to work in order to carry out certain jobs. The permit to work should also document what to do if there are accidents or emergencies.

The Electricity at Work Regulations 1989

Working in a small group, discuss the following safety legislation and produce a short (3–5 minute) presentation, highlighting any areas that may need attention in your workplace. Categorize your points under the headings 'Attitudes', 'Equipment', 'Procedures' and 'Skills'.

The three main hazards of electricity are contact with live parts, fire and explosion. Every year there are about 1 000 accidents involving shock and burning due to electricity, and these are only the ones that are reported. At least 30 of these are fatal.

Fires started by poor electrical installations cause many more deaths and injuries. Explosions can also be caused by electrical apparatus or static electricity igniting flammable vapours or dust.

We often forget that the ordinary 240 volt, 13 amp domestic plug voltage is enough to kill. In business and industry there are far greater risks concerned with the use of electricity, not only because more sophisticated and powerful equipment is used, but also because of the environment and conditions in which it is used.

As a basic summary, here are some of the requirements of these Regulations.

1. Equipment and Conditions

Proper equipment and working conditions must be provided. If possible this means that voltage must be reduced. For instance, lighting can be run at 12 or 25 volts and portable tools must be run at 110 volts from an isolating transformer. Safety devices should be provided and installation must be carried out professionally and in accordance with full safety regulations.

2. Training

All staff using electrical equipment must receive adequate training on and information about safe operation of that equipment and also regarding the dangers of electricity. For instance, would you know what to do if someone received an electric shock?

3. Access and Lighting

Adequate access and lighting must be made available for all electrical installations, and fuse boxes and isolators must be provided.

4. Live Working

Live working must not be allowed on any equipment unless absolutely necessary. Before work begins, equipment and power cables must be isolated and the power removed from the installation.

Proper safe procedures must be documented and enforced. Anyone carrying out electrical work must be competent to do it safely. This may mean bringing in outside contractors. If so, make sure they belong to a body which checks their work, such as the National Inspection Council for Electrical Installation Contractors. Other procedures may involve the insulation and armouring of certain power cables, provision of special plugs, replacing frayed and damaged cables quickly and completely, using special protection equipment, or using special low-voltage equipment in certain situations. You may need to create special procedures to deal with overhead electric lines, particularly on building or construction sites.

6. Safety Inspections

Inspection of all portable apparatus must be done by a competent person on a regular basis, and this inspection must be documented. Any special requirements, such as waterproof or explosion-proof protected equipment, must also be assessed.

▤ The COSHH Regulations 1988

Working in a small group, discuss the following safety legislation and produce a short (3–5 minute) presentation, highlighting any areas that may need attention in your workplace. Categorize your points under the headings 'Attitudes', 'Equipment', 'Procedures' and 'Skills'.

COSHH stands for the 'Control of Substances Hazardous to Health'.

These Regulations were introduced in 1988 and cover all chemicals, products and materials and that may cause damage, injury or discomfort to human beings.

You may also need to consider the Chemicals (Hazard, Information and Packaging) Regulations of 1993. These cover the contents and hazards of any product and must be indicated on the package or label.

Safety data sheets should also be provided with any products you supply.

Many substances can hurt you if they get into your body, even many household everyday substances have potential to cause harm. Special care is needed when handling cancer-causing substances, or flammable, explosive and other more serious types of materials, such as bleaches and toxic substances.

Here are some of the key points as required under the COSHH Regulations.

1. Eliminate or Reduce

Wherever possible you must avoid using hazardous substances. The greatest and the simplest way of reducing risk is to eliminate the product or the hazard completely.

2. Information

It is important that the organization and managers ensure that proper information exists about the hazards and the products and substances themselves. Every hazardous substance must be labelled and have safety data sheets detailing its storage, transportation and the hazards that it presents.

3. Awareness

People using the products should be aware of the hazards, how they could be affected, what to do to keep themselves and others safe, how to use control equipment and personal protection equipment, how to check and spot when things are wrong, and the results of any exposure monitoring or health surveillance that may be carried out. They should also have full knowledge regarding any emergency procedures should a leakage or a spillage occur.

4. Provision of Proper Working Conditions and Procedures

Controls must be put in place, and checks made to ensure that they are maintained. This will include not only the maintenance of plant, equipment and ventilation levels, but also ensuring that people are following the rules. If personal protective equipment is used, this must also be tested and replaced if worn or damaged.

Reproduced from *Health and Safety Games for Trainers*, Graham Roberts-Phelps, Gower, Aldershot   165

Full and adequate training must be provided to all staff who need to use or come into contact with any substance that is considered to be hazardous to health. Asking someone to work with hazardous substances without proper training is an offence under the Regulations.

6. Risk Assessments

Risk assessments must be carried out regularly. These need to consider the hazards of the substances or their ingredients, the route into the body, whether the substances can be breathed in, swallowed or absorbed through the skin and the worst result that could arise. Also assessed are the concentration or conditions likely to cause ill health and whether employees know the first symptoms of over-exposure.

The risk assessment must also calculate who could be exposed (including those exposed accidentally). The assessment must also allow for how often people come into contact with this substance, that is how often or how long they are working with the substance, and how much of it they come into contact with. These assessments must be written and fully documented. Special assessments are required for lead and asbestos, which have their own separate legislation due to the extreme hazards that each of these now present. If you use either of these substances, or are likely to come into contact with them, you must be fully aware of the regulations controlling these.

7. Regular Checks and Health Monitoring

Regular checks and health monitoring may also be required, depending on your level of usage and the substances involved. These may require sampling of air, as well as other medical and health checks. These must be made regularly and records kept, in some cases for as long as 40 years.

The Manual Handling Regulations 1992

Working in a small group, discuss the following safety legislation and produce a short (3–5 minute) presentation, highlighting any areas that may need attention in your workplace. Categorize your points under the headings 'Attitudes', 'Equipment', 'Procedures' and 'Skills'.

The Manual Handling Regulations were introduced in 1992 as part of an EC Directive on Health and Safety. The Workplace Regulations of 1992 also have some emphasis on manual handling operations. The main requirements of these regulations are as follows.

1. Information and Training

All employees must be aware of the common hazards that exist with the manual movement of loads and frequent forced or awkward movements of the body. They must understand how these can lead to back injuries and other injuries in terms of hands, wrists, arms, legs and neck.

2. Safe Practice

Employees should be trained on how to lift safely, as well as how to use any lifting or manual handling equipment or facilities (including hoists, trolleys, trucks and steps) provided.

3. Eliminate or Reduce

It is important that manual handling is eliminated wherever possible. The Regulations state that you must avoid manual handling if a safer way, e.g. a mechanical one, is practical. This may mean designing jobs to fit the work to the person rather than the person to the work. This would take into account human capabilities and limitations and improve efficiency as well as safety. Thus, an organization must avoid manual handling wherever there is a risk of injury. This risk of injury must be properly assessed for any hazardous manual handling operation that cannot be avoided. Therefore, employees should not be asked to lift heavy or awkward objects if they haven't been trained or if the load is above the safe limits and so represents an unreasonable level of risk of injury.

As well as providing mechanical help, such as a sack truck or hoist, other options include making loads smaller or lighter or easier to grasp, changing the system of work to reduce the effort required or perhaps improving the layout of the workplace to make the work more efficient. Protective equipment may also be needed to protect such things as hands and feet when lifting.

4. Lifting Aids

Wherever possible, equipment and lifting aids should be provided. This equipment should be tested and be safe for the use intended. People must be trained in its usage, and it must be regularly maintained.

All manual handling operations must be assessed for risk, and that risk assessment properly documented. One particular hazard that may need special attention is that of repetitive handling. This is where the repeated or awkward movements which are too forceful, too fast or carried out for too long can lead to disorders of the arms, hands or legs. Occupations such as typing, working on a till and assembly work are particularly at risk. The assessment should look at the gripping, squeezing or pressure required, awkward hand or arm movements, repeated or continuous movements, the speed of these movements, the level of intensity and what breaks are afforded to individuals.

The Noise at Work Regulations 1989

Working in a small group, discuss the following safety legislation and produce a short (3–5 minute) presentation, highlighting any areas that may need attention in your workplace. Categorize your points under the headings 'Attitudes', 'Equipment', 'Procedures' and 'Skills'.

Loud noise at work can cause irreversible hearing damage. It accelerates the normal hearing loss which usually occurs as we grow older. It can also cause other problems, such as tinnitus, and interfere with communication, which in turn can cause great personal stress. The Noise at Work Regulations of 1989 are intended to reduce hearing damage caused by loud noise and they lay down three action levels. They require employees to take action when noise reaches the first action level of 85 decibels. They should take further action if it reaches the second action level of 90 decibels or the third action level of 40 decibels. The key requirements of the Regulations include the following.

1. Correct Noise Monitoring

The noise levels in any workplace must be assessed with the proper sophisticated equipment. However, if you cannot hear clearly what someone is saying when you are about two metres away, the level is likely to be around 85 decibels or higher, and if you cannot hear someone clearly when you are about one metre away, the level is likely to be around 90 decibels or higher. If you consider that the noise from a loud radio in a normal room is probably around 70–75 decibels, that standing on the pavement of a busy street is between 80–85 decibels and that standing very close to a heavy lorry would be about 90–100 decibels, you can see that it doesn't take a lot of noise to begin to put hearing at risk.

2. Noise Levels

The Regulations require that noise is kept below certain levels and the workplace is categorized accordingly. The first level, where noise does not exceed 85 decibels, is a normal working environment. However, it is necessary to make protection freely available to those who want it or request it where the level exceeds 85 decibels. At the second action level, where noise exceeds 90 decibels, these areas must be properly marked, and hearing protection must be made mandatory. However, it is important to remember that hearing protection is no substitute for noise reduction or eliminating the hazard in the first place.

3. Ear Protection

Proper ear protection must be provided for and worn by all employees, and others, who either request it or are required to work in a second or third action zone. Employers must ensure that the hearing protection is fitted correctly and is worn properly. It should be regularly checked and maintained for comfort and convenience. This equipment should be made available at no cost.

4. Training

All employees working in noisy areas must be fully trained, on not only the hazards but also on the wearing of protective hearing equipment. Information and advice must be made freely available and should be clearly displayed.

5. Hearing Tests

Hearing tests should be made available to all workers working in high noise areas, and should be made available to any workers who think that their hearing is being affected as a result of noise at work.

6. Reduction of Noise

The Regulations emphasize the importance of reducing noise by eliminating the source of the noise in the first place, rather than just by protecting workers from that noise. This may mean changing equipment or machinery, organizing the workplace differently or using acoustic enclosures wherever possible.

📄 The Fire Precautions Act 1971

Working in a small group, discuss the following safety legislation and produce a short (3–5 minute) presentation, highlighting any areas that may need attention in your workplace. Categorize your points under the headings 'Attitudes', 'Equipment', 'Procedures' and 'Skills'.

Depending on your type of building, the kind of business and the number of people employed in the building, you may need a fire certificate. Your local fire authority can offer advice in this area.

You must have clear and well-communicated fire procedures which are tested regularly. This includes fire drills and ensuring staff know what to do in the event of discovering a fire or having to phone for emergency services.

All reasonable steps must be taken to prevent a fire occurring in the first place and to reduce the risk of fire. This may mean reconsidering the type of equipment, materials and substances that you are using and how they are stored. If you are using flammable liquids, can this be reduced, eliminated or kept to a restricted area?

All staff must be trained in safety procedures, and information should be made freely available regarding the use of fire equipment and fire exits.

Regular checks must be made on all fire safety equipment. This should be documented and must include all extinguishers, fire alarms and other forms of fire emergency equipment. In addition, fire doors and escape routes must be checked, both in terms of operation and to ensure that the fire regulations are not being breached.

The company should have clear procedures and regulations regarding precautions to safeguard against fire and what to do in the unfortunate event of a fire occurring. The Act requires both employers and employees to take every practical measure in ensuring these regulations are fully implemented.

Reproduced from *Health and Safety Games for Trainers*, Graham Roberts-Phelps, Gower, Aldershot

The Display Screen Equipment Regulations 1992

Working in a small group, discuss the following safety legislation and produce a short (3–5 minute) presentation, highlighting any areas that may need attention in your workplace. Categorize your points under the headings 'Attitudes', 'Equipment', 'Procedures' and 'Skills'.

These Regulations have been introduced to meet the needs of the changing nature of our workplaces and offices. Over the last ten years the use of computers and visual display units (VDUs) has greatly increased. Workers using VDUs need well-designed work areas with suitable lighting and comfortable adjustable seating. This helps to reduce eye strain and back or upper limb problems. No special precautions are necessary against radiation.

The Regulations require the following.

1. Assessment

All work stations must be assessed regularly and a record kept of that assessment. This is best done at least once every 12 months, more often if the work load or equipment is changed.

2. Improvements

Any changes or improvements to equipment or working practices noted in the written assessment must be fully implemented under the guidelines within the Regulations.

3. Safety Training

All staff who are classified as habitual users of VDUs or display screen equipment must be trained in safe working practices. They should also be made aware of the health and safety aspects of their work.

4. Health Monitoring

Organizations should also monitor health problems of people using VDUs. There are obligations to provide eye tests for users on request and at regular intervals afterwards, and in certain cases special spectacles if required.

5. Work Loads

Work loads must be organized and planned so there are breaks or changes of activity. This is to avoid undue stress, which may be represented in the form of headaches, backaches or general fatigue.

Reproduced from *Health and Safety Games for Trainers*, Graham Roberts-Phelps, Gower, Aldershot

The Workplace Regulations (Health, Safety and Welfare) 1992

Working in a small group, discuss the following safety legislation and produce a short (3–5 minute) presentation, highlighting any areas that may need attention in your workplace. Categorize your points under the headings 'Attitudes', 'Equipment', 'Procedures' and 'Skills'.

There can be many dangers at work. Safety hazards include slips, trips and falls, as well as more obvious things, such as fire, electricity and hazardous chemicals. Health hazards may also include poor seating, lighting, building repair and ventilation. These Regulations require the assessment of working environments and provide a set of guidelines with which to do this. The Regulations apply in full now to new or modified workplaces and to existing ones from January 1996. Before then, similar previous requirements (e.g. the Factories Act 1961 and the Offices, Shops and Railway Premises Act 1963) applied.

The main requirements of these Regulations are as follows.

1. Lighting

An organization must provide good light, this means natural light wherever possible, which avoids glare. A good level of local lighting is required where detailed work is carried out. Lighting must be of a suitable form. Some fluorescent tubes flicker and can be dangerous with some types of rotating machinery. Special fittings are required where flammable or explosive atmospheres or equipment may be used.

2. Heating and Ventilation

A reasonable working temperature must exist, usually at least 16°C or 13°C where strenuous work is performed. Local heating or cooling should be provided where a comfortable temperature cannot be maintained, for instance in large warehouse areas. Good ventilation must be provided especially in areas where fumes or dust may exist, and draughts should be avoided. Heating systems should also be checked to establish that they do not give off dangerous or offensive levels of fumes into the workplace.

3. Hygiene

The Regulations specify there should be sufficient toilets, changing and washing facilities. These include separate toilets for men and women (unless each convenience has its own lockable door), wash basins with hot (or warm) and cold running water, showers for dirty work or emergencies, soap and towels or a hand-dryer, and skin cleansers with nail brushes where necessary. In certain situations, special hygiene precautions are required, for instance in the serving and preparation of food. A clean drinking water supply should also be made available, together with rest facilities. The Regulations also specify that an organization must provide arrangements to protect non-smokers from the discomfort caused by tobacco smoke in any rest area, for example by providing separate areas or rooms for smokers and non-smokers or by prohibiting smoking in rest areas and rest rooms.

Employees should be able to move around the premises safely. This means safe routes for pedestrians and vehicles, level and even surfaces without broken boards, obstructions or holes. Hand-rails should be fitted on stairways and ramps where necessary. Safe vision panels should be installed in swing-doors, and surfaces must be maintained so as not to be slippery. Passage ways and stairways must also be well lit and kept clear of obstacles and obstructions.

5. Equipment

The Regulations require that safety equipment be provided and maintained, and that provisions are made appropriate to the place of work.

The Management of Health and Safety at Work Regulations 1992

Working in a small group, discuss the following safety legislation and produce a short (3–5 minute) presentation, highlighting any areas that may need attention in your workplace. Categorize your points under the headings 'Attitudes', 'Equipment', 'Procedures' and 'Skills'.

These regulations make specific demands on managers and directors, as well as on health and safety officers, with regard to their responsibilities in assessing and managing risk. Described simply, this means identifying hazards and quantifying and reducing risk.

A hazard can be defined as anything that has the potential to cause harm, such as chemicals, electricity and working from ladders. Risk is the chance – either big or small – of harm actually being done. For example, consider a can of solvent on a shelf. There is a hazard if the solvent is toxic or flammable, but very little risk. However, the risk will increase when it is taken down and poured into a bucket. Harmful vapour is given off and there is a danger of spillage. Things are made much worse if a mop is then used to spread it over the floor for cleaning. The chance of harm, i.e. the risk, is then high. This is known as risk assessment.

Here are the main requirements of these Regulations.

1. Competence

Any risk assessment must be carried out by someone who is regarded as competent. This is someone who has the necessary technical expertise, training and experience to carry out the examination or test. This could be a person from an outside organization, such as an insurance company, or a member of staff. That person should not only know the health and safety aspects, but also have a good understanding of the job and the task involved.

2. Regularity

Assessments should be made regularly and in writing.

3. Implementation

Assessments must be acted on. Carrying out risk assessments and identifying hazards and risks is not enough. Recommendations must be implemented.

4. Training

All members of staff should receive proper health and safety training at regular intervals. This training should be appropriate to both their level of experience, responsibility and the tasks required of them.

Reproduced from *Health and Safety Games for Trainers*, Graham Roberts-Phelps, Gower, Aldershot

Discussion Groups 1 and 2

Trainer's notes

Outline	
Format:	*Small groups*
Type:	*Discussion*
Time:	*10 minutes, plus discussion*
Resources:	*Handout provided, flip chart*

Objective

To share experiences and demonstrate that accidents and mishaps can, and do, happen to us all.

Procedure

Give the handout provided to the delegates.

Ask them to follow the instructions on the handout.

After 10 minutes, gather responses, transfer them onto a flip chart and discuss.

Discussion Group 1: Safety Awareness

Find recent examples and experiences of these accidents, injuries and illnesses. List them under the appropriate heading. (They can be at work or at home.)

See if you can get a 'full house'.

Back pain or backache	Cuts and bruises	Slips, trips or falls
General aches and pains	**Headaches and tiredness**	**Car accident or near miss**
Bumps and bruises	**Electric shock**	**Burns and scalds**

Reproduced from *Health and Safety Games for Trainers*, Graham Roberts-Phelps, Gower, Aldershot

📄 Discussion Group 2: Hazards and Risks

Discuss the following question, listing your responses in the space provided.

- *What hazards and risks exist in your office?*

Give several examples and be specific. Keep in mind that a hazard is something that has the potential to cause pain, injury or discomfort (whether an object, process, environment or standard). A risk is what may happen and the chance of it happening.

Hazards	Risks

Now identify ways that these hazards can be avoided and the risks reduced.

Hazard or risk	Way to avoid it

Reproduced from *Health and Safety Games for Trainers*, Graham Roberts-Phelps, Gower, Aldershot

Case Study: Accident Report

Trainer's notes

Outline	
Format:	*Pairs/small groups*
Type:	*Discussion/problem solver*
Time:	*10 minutes, plus discussion*
Resources:	*Handout provided*

Objective

To introduce the theme of human error in relation to health and safety and the importance of personal responsibility.

Procedure

Give the handout provided to the delegates.

Ask them to read the case study accident report given on the handout.

Ask the following questions:

- What do you think caused the accident?

- Who was at fault?

Delegates should be as specific as possible in their replies.

After 10 minutes, gather responses and discuss.

📄 Accident Report Case Study

'Whilst securing scaffolding in preparation for the rendering of a school wall and repair of roof tiles, three poles and six clamps were dropped from a height of 30 feet when an inexperienced and unsupervised sub-contractor slipped.

They caused over £2 000 of damage to a company vehicle and, more seriously, injured three people, causing serious head injuries to one of them. Altogether they spent over eight weeks off work. However, because two of them were not wearing safety helmets they received no compensation and received written warnings, as this broke company regulations. Work was delayed by three days whilst the accident was investigated, which in turn caused delays to other work. The cost of this disruption was considerable.'

 Reproduced from *Health and Safety Games for Trainers*, Graham Roberts-Phelps, Gower, Aldershot

Problems, Causes and Solutions

Trainer's notes

Outline	
Format:	*Pairs or small groups*
Type:	*Problem-solving/discussion*
Time:	*20 minutes, plus discussion*
Resources:	*Paper, the handout provided*

Objective

The purpose of this exercise is to identify the links between safety, poor working practices and their effects.

Procedure

First, ask delegates to list health and safety hazards, problems or issues that face them as a manager. They should then review the list and rank them in order of importance or concern. Allow 10 minutes.

Example of problems include the following. You could use them as illustrations of the task or as prompts.

- People are not very safety aware or act dangerously.

- The office layout means that walking through it is difficult.

- Plug sockets are overloaded with adapters and extension leads.

- The lighting is poor or there are not sufficient blinds to block sunlight.

- Corridors and passage ways are often used as storage areas or lined with boxes.

- Some equipment is poorly maintained.

- People do not always have a proper break.

- Safety issues are not discussed regularly.

- Computers/VDUs are set up incorrectly and do not conform to safety standards.

- People often feel tired and stressed.

- Sharp objects are often left out when not in use.

- Chemicals in the office are not stored or labelled correctly.

- Drinks are placed on or near electrical appliances.

- Papers and files are often stacked on top of computers and printers.

- People often attempt to fix photocopiers themselves.

- There are no steps or ladders to reach high shelves.

- People have to lift heavy objects frequently.

- There are trailing cables or ripped carpet/flooring.

- Shelves and filing cabinets are overstacked.

Give delegates the handout provided. Ask them to list their issues (starting with the most important) in the problem column. Next they should decide on probable causes and possible solutions.

After 10 minutes, gather responses and discuss.

📄 Problems, Causes and Solutions

Problem	Cause	Solution
1.		
2.		
3.		
4.		
5.		
6.		
7.		
8.		
9.		
10.		

9. Crossword and Word Search Puzzles

Crosswords 1–5, Word Searches 1–5

Trainer's notes

Outline	
Format:	*Individuals*
Type:	*Ice-breaker/energizer*
Time:	*15 minutes*
Resources:	*Handouts provided, flip chart (optional)*

Objective

A fun way to reiterate the key terms and issues.

Procedure

Give the delegates one of the handouts provided. For the Word Search puzzles, you could give the word list which goes with the puzzle or withhold the list to make it more difficult.

After 15 minutes, or as soon as the first person has completed it (if you are making it competitive), gather responses and give the results (in the answer section). You could transfer the answer onto the flip chart for ease.

📄 Crossword 1: Office Safety Awareness

Across

4. Clean

5. R-kiss (anagram)

6. Look after

7. Statement of fact or something you must do

9. Don't be the cause of one

11. Messy

12. Too much

14. Can be an obstacle

15. Legislation

16. You have to do this to be informed

Down

1. Cutting edge

2. Before help arrives

3. Heat

6. Messy area

8. Red for …

10. Split

11. Run across

13. Sharp shock

📄 Crossword 2: Display Screen Equipment

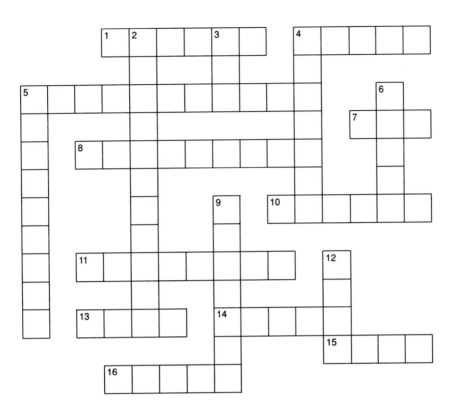

Across

1. Modify

4. A small rodent

5. Not a railway station (2 words 4–7)

7. Not to wipe your feet on

8. Chair/desk/VDU

10. Your printer needs this

11. Put them up on this

13. Relax

14. The ideal in-tray

15. Opposite of 'go'

16. Produce a hard copy

Down

2. Noisy interruptions

3. The right position

4. Screen

5. A helping hand for your feet

6. The telegram?

9. Stop in time

12. Tap tap tap

Crossword 3: Risk Assessment

Across

2. Employed here
5. Bringing to a standard
8. A need
10. Keep from injury
11. Estimate its worth
13. Stop before it happens
14. Could be harmful
15. Personal damage

Down

1. Looking after premises
3. State of the environment
4. Unexpected event
6. Knowing
7. Fines
9. Can cause accidents
12. Mistake

Crossword 4: Safety for Managers

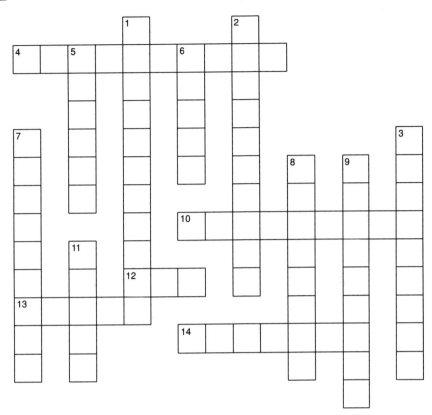

Across

4. Health and Safety _____

10. Place of employment

12. Legislation

13. Bad for the cars

14. Cleanliness

Down

1. Morally obliged

2. Series of actions

3. Common purpose

5. Keeps well

6. Wires can cause these

7. Trips and falls, for example

8. Your responsibility

9. Looking out

11. Wet conditions can cause this

Reproduced from *Health and Safety Games for Trainers*, Graham Roberts-Phelps, Gower, Aldershot

📄 Crossword 5: Environmental Awareness

Across

1. Chemicals can cause
4. Use again
6. Offensive product
7. Make better
8. Tiring pollution
10. Look after
13. Waste
14. Toxic, for example

Down

2. Gas around the planet
3. Save
5. Drive
9. Poison
11. Pollution on the move
12. Noxious fumes

 Reproduced from *Health and Safety Games for Trainers*, Graham Roberts-Phelps, Gower, Aldershot

📄 Word Search 1: Office Safety Awareness

D	I	A	T	S	R	I	F	D	Q	S	B	M	J	H
V	E	R	A	C	O	B	S	T	A	C	L	E	X	H
Z	C	D	N	B	P	I	R	T	R	N	B	R	C	B
M	I	L	A	M	C	A	Y	Z	F	A	G	E	G	R
G	F	S	U	O	I	C	S	N	O	C	E	E	R	C
V	F	M	B	N	L	J	T	A	R	I	J	U	R	M
F	O	T	I	S	N	R	N	T	F	B	L	U	Z	L
P	B	N	H	Y	G	I	E	N	E	E	J	L	Y	Y
C	G	A	M	U	L	T	D	V	S	D	T	B	P	O
H	R	R	V	A	C	R	I	K	O	A	G	Y	A	Y
P	A	D	P	X	A	Q	C	Z	R	A	U	D	C	S
Z	F	I	F	Z	F	G	C	V	L	Q	V	Q	P	T
A	Y	D	A	I	H	K	A	O	Q	U	L	D	Z	B
T	M	H	G	S	G	S	V	K	I	T	O	X	L	M

📄 Words for Word Search 1

ACCIDENTS

CARE

CONSCIOUS

DANGER

FIRST AID

HAZARD

HYGIENE

OBSTACLE

OFFICE

OVERLOADED

RULES

SAFETY

SHARP

TRAINING

TRIP

 Reproduced from *Health and Safety Games for Trainers*, Graham Roberts-Phelps, Gower, Aldershot

Word Search 2: Display Screen Equipment

S	Y	V	V	P	U	U	N	T	J	P	L	T	F	B
M	A	F	F	S	H	L	S	O	Y	F	S	C	B	X
U	H	K	W	T	N	E	M	P	I	U	Q	E	L	Q
F	S	B	Z	G	R	I	A	I	J	T	H	U	M	L
C	L	U	T	T	E	R	U	D	N	C	I	S	N	V
F	C	L	S	E	L	B	A	C	A	A	R	S	Q	S
D	I	I	E	U	H	M	W	K	C	C	S	I	O	S
T	R	Q	R	K	Z	R	C	A	K	J	H	N	M	P
W	K	A	T	S	Y	A	D	F	D	G	L	E	G	B
I	T	M	O	A	B	W	X	I	L	X	C	N	W	S
S	C	G	O	B	Z	S	G	A	E	I	P	W	X	C
T	F	U	F	E	Y	M	R	A	I	U	Z	E	W	L
I	J	A	H	P	N	E	H	Y	Q	A	M	A	H	C
N	Q	I	W	V	L	B	K	K	O	B	V	N	H	X
G	E	H	I	F	J	S	I	W	D	T	R	P	Q	Q

📄 Words for Word Search 2

ADJUST

BACKACHE

CABLES

CLUTTER

EQUIPMENT

FOOTREST

GLARE

HEADACHE

KEYBOARD

POSITION

TILT

TWISTING

WRIST REST

 Reproduced from *Health and Safety Games for Trainers*, Graham Roberts-Phelps, Gower, Aldershot

📄 Word Search 3: Risk Assessment

M	R	A	S	E	I	R	U	J	N	I	H	R	E	S
A	E	C	N	A	N	E	T	N	I	A	M	S	J	E
N	Q	A	S	S	E	S	S	M	E	N	T	S	Y	Z
U	U	Y	M	P	Y	P	L	A	I	F	Z	E	U	E
A	I	U	Y	E	O	O	Q	N	H	C	P	N	X	Q
L	R	U	D	N	R	N	V	A	O	O	S	E	K	L
H	E	E	S	A	U	S	H	G	L	N	D	R	A	E
A	M	N	R	L	Z	I	H	E	G	D	R	A	D	C
N	E	X	W	T	Q	B	S	R	F	I	X	W	N	T
D	N	P	Y	I	C	L	O	S	I	T	C	A	E	H
L	T	R	Y	E	L	E	C	T	R	I	C	I	T	Y
I	S	D	C	S	R	O	R	R	E	O	O	S	K	M
N	S	A	M	L	G	V	D	L	T	N	I	Q	K	E
G	P	U	T	H	A	Z	A	R	D	S	C	I	D	R

📄 Words for Word Search 3

ASSESSMENTS

AWARENESS

CONDITIONS

COSHH

ELECTRICITY

ERRORS

FIRE

HAZARDS

INJURIES

MAINTENANCE

MANAGERS

MANUAL HANDLING

PENALTIES

REQUIREMENTS

RESPONSIBLE

Reproduced from *Health and Safety Games for Trainers*, Graham Roberts-Phelps, Gower, Aldershot

📄 Word Search 4: Safe Manual Handling

E	A	V	T	A	K	R	H	V	I	F	F	D	K	W
O	T	J	E	S	U	O	U	N	E	R	T	S	M	V
M	T	N	E	M	P	I	U	Q	E	T	H	G	M	G
H	I	H	I	S	Y	C	S	E	I	R	U	J	N	I
P	T	A	P	Q	Z	P	F	A	L	S	T	I	K	Z
O	U	G	N	I	Y	R	R	A	C	B	T	X	O	U
S	D	N	H	B	O	L	A	O	A	F	E	O	H	N
T	E	I	M	M	V	Y	H	D	I	M	I	M	O	M
U	F	L	R	Z	U	V	B	L	S	S	L	F	U	P
R	O	I	U	H	Q	A	U	K	O	J	B	N	R	M
E	S	A	L	R	C	E	D	A	O	K	H	P	W	N
K	Z	R	Z	K	K	H	N	G	L	J	T	X	Q	U
P	H	T	W	Z	R	M	G	I	C	K	H	T	I	C
J	L	T	S	E	V	O	L	G	P	E	U	J	N	K
J	R	I	V	Y	J	C	F	M	U	S	A	U	B	L

📄 Words for Word Search 4

ATTITUDE

BAD BACK

CARRYING

EQUIPMENT

FORKLIFT

FREE FROM RISK

GLOVES

HEAVY

INJURIES

LIFTING

POSTURE

RULES

SPINE

STOOP

STRENUOUS

TRAILING

Reproduced from *Health and Safety Games for Trainers*, Graham Roberts-Phelps, Gower, Aldershot

Word Search 5: Environmental Awareness

E	R	E	H	P	S	O	M	T	A	F	H	O	E	K
N	G	C	V	O	S	W	E	J	K	P	B	R	N	N
V	C	O	E	L	C	Y	C	E	R	G	K	I	C	K
I	Z	N	M	L	I	G	B	J	B	E	K	K	S	P
R	O	O	K	U	F	R	E	T	S	A	W	S	N	D
O	I	M	C	T	R	E	N	O	Z	O	U	K	D	X
N	K	Y	H	I	V	N	M	X	Y	B	X	J	X	C
M	D	S	E	O	J	E	F	I	U	R	P	P	D	Z
E	X	H	A	N	F	E	S	N	T	M	I	T	J	C
N	J	T	P	I	B	R	D	Z	B	A	A	R	M	R
T	M	R	E	H	B	G	A	N	R	Y	N	E	R	S
A	W	A	R	E	N	E	S	S	Q	U	V	K	C	I
L	G	E	H	Y	I	D	P	W	L	R	C	M	Z	Y

📄 Words for Word Search 5

ATMOSPHERE

AWARENESS

CHEAPER

EARTH

ECONOMY

ENERGY

ENVIRONMENTAL

GREEN

OZONE

POLLUTION

RECYCLE

TOXIN

WASTE

10. Answers

2. True/False Quizzes

Quiz 1: Safety Awareness

1. True, apart from 'Acts of God'
2. True
3. False
4. True
5. True
6. False
7. True
8. False, it also covers visitors
9. True
10. True

Quiz 2: Safety Awareness

1. True
2. True
3. True, employers must remove hazards and eliminate risks
4. True
5. True
6. True
7. True
8. True
9. True
10. True

Quiz 3: Display Screen Equipment

1. True
2. True
3. True
4. True

5. True

6. True

7. True

8. True

9. True

10. False

Quiz 4: Risk Assessment

1. True, apart from 'Acts of God'

2. False

3. True

4. False

5. True

6. False

7. False, it is every 12 months at least

8. True

9. False, it is 30 million

10. True

Quiz 5: Safety for Managers

1. False

2. True

3. False

4. True

5. True, the number is 600

6. True, followed by slips and trips

7. True

8. False, the essentials are: 1. heat and ventilation, 2. toilet and washing facilities, 3. safety notices (*and 4., of course, digestive biscuits!*).

9. False, safety inspectors have the right of entry, and the right to interview and take samples with or without an organization's permission

10. False, it is every 12 months or if conditions or work routines change significantly

Quiz 6: Environmental Awareness

1. True, 2.2 gallons for every flush
2. True
3. True
4. True
5. True
6. True
7. True
8. True
9. True
10. True

Quiz 7: Safe Manual Handling

1. True
2. True
3. True
4. True
5. True
6. True
7. True
8. True
9. False, everybody, in every job, is at risk
10. True

Quiz 8: Fire Safety

1. True
2. True
3. True
4. True, it contains hazardous substances
5. True
6. True

7. True

8. True

9. All True

10. False

Quiz 9: COSHH Safety

1. True

2. False, it is not always convenient, but it is necessary

3. False

4. True

5. True

6. True

7. False

8. True

9. True

10. False, it is a joint responsibility

3. Knowledge Tests

Test 1: Safety Awareness

1. 1. Provide adequate training and supervision

   2. Provide PPE if needed

   3. Create safe working procedures

2. 1. Follow safety rules

   2. Use care and consideration

   3. Wear any safety equipment that is provided

3. 1. Manual handling

   2. Display screen equipment

   3. Workplace regulations

4. 1. Heat and ventilation

   2. Toilet and washing facilities

   3. Safety notices

5. 1. Electric equipment

   2. Lifting operations

   3. Display screen equipment

6. 1. Slips, trips and falls

   2. Manual handling

   3. Poor configuration of computer work stations

7. A hazard is a danger, a risk is the chance of that danger turning into an accident or injury

8. True

9. (b) 1 600 000

Test 2: Safety at Work

1. (c) 30 million

2. Back injury, followed by slips and trips

3. (b) 600

4. 1. Laziness, 2. Not following instructions, 3. Showing off

5. 1. Taking safety seriously, 2. Finding out information, 3. Spotting hazards and risk

6. 3. 2 200 000

7. (b) 16°C

8. This depends on your situation

9. 1. Not bending your legs when picking up heavy loads, 2. Not checking the weight of the load before lifting, 3. Not holding the load close to the body

10. 1. Check safety procedures, 2. Follow safety guidelines and procedures, 3. Ensure staff are properly trained in safety techniques

Test 3: Fire Safety

1. 1. Raise the alarm, 2. Call the fire services, 3. Evacuate the building

2. Speaking clearly and slowly, you should give the telephone number of the phone from which you are calling and your exact location (displayed on the telephone or near the telephone box). This should then be followed by a clear description of the nature of the fire, its exact location and any other important information such as vehicles in the area, people involved or hazardous or explosive substances that may be nearby

3. 1. Red (water), 2. Black (CO_2), 3. Cream (foam), 4. Blue (powder)

4. 1. Remove the pin or catch, 2. Aim the nozzle at base of fire, 3. Squeeze the lever firmly

5. Panic, smoke, flames

6. 1. Shut all doors, 2. Close the windows, 3. Turn off the ventilation system

7. Turn off the power and locate the black fire extinguisher

8. 1. Oxygen, 2. Flammable liquids, 3. Fuel/heat

9. As well as the obvious fire hazards, other hazards could include: cluttered walkways, old or badly maintained electrical equipment, flammable substances etc.

10. 2. Turn off the valve and move the cylinder outside

Test 4: Manual Handling

1. (a) 5.5 million

2. 1. Heavy objects, 2. Awkward objects, 3. Dirty or wet objects

3. 1. Pause, 2. Bend, 3. Grip, 4. Look, 5. Lift, 6. Hold

4. Manual Handling Regulations 1992

5. 15–25 kg

6. The weight, size, shape and condition of object. Plan the activity. Consider protective clothing and lifting aids.

7. Back strain, slipped disk or pulled muscle

8. Position of feet, getting a sure grip and lifting with the knees

9. 30 per cent

10. (b) 20 days

Test 5: COSHH

1. Control of substances hazardous to health

2. Anything able or liable to cause harm either through breathing, intake or contact

3. 1. Cleaning fluid, 2. Paint fumes, 3. Petrol

4. 1. Cleaning substances, 2. Bleach, 3. Pills and medicines

5. 1. Lead, 2. Asbestos

6. 1. Substances

   2. Legislation

   3. Work being done

7. 1. Hazards and risks

   2. Operation and storage

   3. Emergency procedures

8. Chemical hazard identification and packaging

9. 1. Read instructions

   2. Wear required or recommended PPE

   3. Providing and maintaining good ventilation

10. Extreme or regular exposure to very toxic substances

Test 6: Display Screen Equipment

1. 1. Stress, 2. Lighting, 3. Environment, 4. Equipment, 5. Posture

2. 1. Backache, 2. Eye soreness, 3. Headaches (also possible pain in shoulders/upper arms, tenderness in wrists/finger joints and stiff neck)

3. 1. Monitor (tilt and swivel base), 2. Chair, 3. Desk space (also possible glare from lights or windows, footrest, document holder and wrist rest)

4. (e) All of the above

5. Every 12 months, at least

6. A competent person

7. (b) Level

8. (b) 18 inches

9. False, there is no proof of this, although if somebody is concerned it is best to seek further advice

Test 7: Display Screen Equipment

1. Visual display monitor

2. Visual Display Unit

3. Input device

4. Moving input device

5. To place the mouse on

6. Central Processing Unit

7. Used to store data

8. A study of how to achieve maximum efficiency

9. Prints pages from your screen when instructed

10. Your CPU

11. Repetitive Strain Injury

12. Softens flare from room lights or window

13. Helps to bring the body into the correct position to use the CPU

14. Holds copy work

15. Light and heat, and generally a 'comfortable' work environment

16. To rest wrist at correct angle and to reduce strain

17. What you see is what you get

18. Static can build up and cause problems (electro-static)

Test 8: Risk Assessment

1. Identifying hazards and quantifying and reducing risk

2. To reduce risks and make the workplace safer and healthier

3. Hazard: a harm that can happen

    Risk: the chance of that happening

4. Employees, contractors and customers

5. 1. Display screen equipment, 2. VDU regulations, 3. PPE

6. (a) All employees

7. No

8. 1. Reduced accidents, 2. Fewer breakdowns/stoppages and less sickness, 3. Better productivity

9. 1. Safe working conditions, 2. Better productivity (keep on top of workload, less hassle, bonus, etc.), 3. Better work environment

10. Be aware of your company electrical boards and answer from your knowledge, consult qualified electricians

Test 9: Safety for Managers

1. 1. Electrical equipment, 2. Lifting operations. 3. Hazardous chemicals

2. 1. Slips, trips and falls, 2. Manual handling, 3. Working from heights, falls

3. A hazard is a danger, a risk is the chance of that danger turning into an accident or injury

4. 1. Examine the load first, 2. Bend your legs, 3. Hold it close to the body

5. 1. Wiring and trailing leads, 2. Fuse loading, 3. Worn cables

6. 1. Trailing leads, 2. Ripped or damaged flooring, 3. Wet conditions

7. 1. Provide adequate training and supervision, 2. Provide PPE if needed, 3. Create safe working procedures

8. 1. Follow safety rules, 2. Use care and consideration, 3. Wear safety equipment that is provided

9. True

10. 1. Manual handling, 2. Display screen equipment, 3. PPE regulations

Test 10: Environmental Awareness

1. (c) 1 million

2. (b) 300 million

3. (a) 85 per cent

4. (b) 10 000

5. (c) 1 000 tons

6. (a) 30 per cent

7. (b) 60 per cent

8. (b) 60 per cent

9. (c) 1 per cent

10. (a) 150 million miles

11. (c) 6 miles

12. (c) 2 250 gallons

6. Ice-breakers

Quiz 1: Safety Signs

1. No smoking
2. Fire extinguishers
3. Poisons
4. Radiation
5. No fires
6. Warning or hazard
7. Inflammable substances
8. Fire phone
9. Ear protection must be worn
10. Slippery surface
11. Hard hat area
12. First aid post
13. Electrical danger
14. Handwash station

Quiz 2: First Aid

1. Temporarily cover the wound with sterile gauze and get medical attention immediately.
2. Control any bleeding by applying firm pressure on either side of object. Drape piece of gauze over the wound and get medical attention.
3. Dial 999. Remove casualty from danger and into fresh air. Place in recovery position.
4. Arrange urgent removal to hospital. If able to drink, give water or milk to sip.
5. Aim to protect casualty. Let them sit down in a quiet place and remove any possible sources of harm. Talk calmly and reassuringly to them, if advisable call a doctor.
6. If the casualty remains unconscious after three minutes, dial 999 for an ambulance. Place in recovery position. If casualty regains full consciousness, watch closely for any deterioration in the level of response. Advise casualty to see his or her doctor.
7. Assess the damage and act accordingly, take recommendations.
8. Assess the situation. Establish whether the casualty is fully conscious or is unconscious but breathing. Make the area safe (by evacuating people or removing the hazard), telephone for assistance, control bleeding or support a limb. Observe the casualty continuously until expert help arrives.

9. Cold compress. Watch for possible concussion.

10. Raise and support foot to minimize swelling. Apply an ice pack or compress. Take or send casualty to hospital. Support limb.

11. Ask the person to sit down. Keep him or her warm and use comforting language until emergency services arrive.

Quiz 3: Health and Safety Jargon

1. Hazard = obstacle or situation with the potential to cause danger; 2. Risk = chance of bad or dangerous consequences; 3. COSHH = control of substances hazardous to health; 4. PPE = personal protective equipment; 5. RSI = repetitive strain injury; 6. Risk-assessment = review of a potentially hazardous situation; 7. Carcinogen = cancer-producing substance; 8. Tinnitus = ringing in the ears; 9. Dermatitis = inflammation of the skin; 10. White finger = caused by excessive vibration; 11. Sciatica = neuralgia of the hip or thigh caused by the sciatic nerve; 12. VDU = visual display unit; 13. EEC Standard = conformity measure set by the European Economic Community; 14. Recycle = convert to reusable material; 15. CPU = central processing unit; 16. LPG = liquefied petroleum gas; 17. HSE = Health and Safety Executive; 18. Ozone = atmospheric layer surrounding the Earth that filters the harmful rays of the Sun; 19. CFC = chlorofluorocarbon

Word Challenge 1

Den Cat Ten Net Nit Tin Din Can Nat Eat Dan Ice

End Cad Tan Ace Act Ant Die Tie And Tea

Word Challenge 2

Men Man Tan Mat Sat Rat Tar Tea Sea Net Nit Rim Sin Sit Sir Tie

Ten Ass Tin Ski Ear Set See Ran Met Kit Are Aim Irk Kin

Discussion: Errors in Lifting

This will depend on your own situation.

Brainteaser 1: Spot the Difference

Answer: (d)

Brainteaser 2: Nine Dots

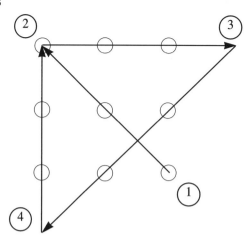

Brainteaser 3: The Dream

Solution: The sacked employee was the warehouse night watchman. He should have been awake all night on security duty. Having a dream proved that he was asleep on the job. For this, he was fired.

Brainteaser 4: World War I

The number of recorded head injuries increased, but the number of deaths decreased. Previously, if a soldier had been hit on the head with a piece of shrapnel, it would have pierced his cap and killed him. This would have been recorded as a death, not a head injury. After helmets were issued, it was more likely that a piece of shrapnel would have caused an injury, not a death. Thus, the incidence of head injuries increased, and the number of deaths decreased.

7. Group Energizers

Quiz 1: Road Safety

1. (c)
2. (b)
3. (a)
4. (c)
5. (c)
6. (d)
7. (b)
8. (b)
9. (a)
10. (c)
11. (b) and (d)
12. (a)
13. (c)
14. (d)
15. (b)

Quiz 2: Road Safety

1. (a)
2. (a) and (d)
3. (c)
4. (d)
5. (d)
6. (c)
7. (a)
8. (a)
9. (c), (d) and (f)
10. (c)
11. (d) and (f)

12. (c)

13. (a)

14. (b)

15. (d)

Putting a Price on It

An example is: Losing an eye: £2000

9. Crossword and Word Search Puzzles

Crossword 1: Office Safety Awareness

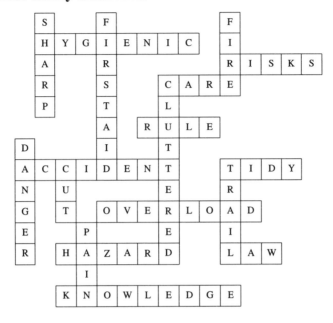

Crossword 2: Display Screen Equipment

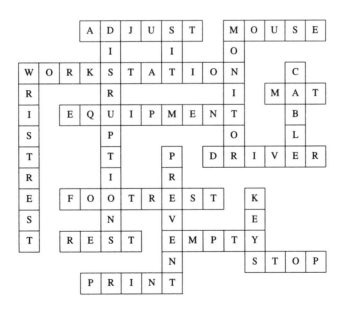

Crossword 3: Risk Assessment

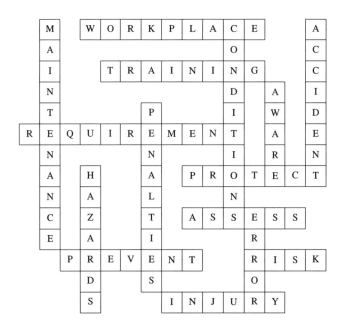

Crossword 4: Safety for Managers

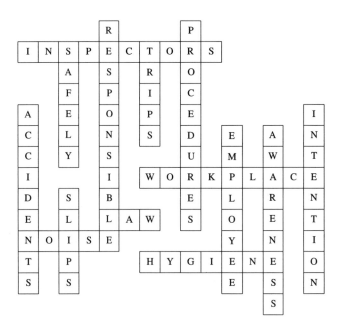

Crossword 5: Environmental Awareness

```
D  A  M  A  G  E              E
      T        R  E  C  Y  C  L  E
      M                    O     N
      P  O  L  L  U  T  I  O  N  E
      S                    O     R
   I  M  P  R  O  V  E      M     G
      H                    I     Y
      E  X  H  A  U  S  T  S
T     R                    E
P  R  O  T  E  C  T      G
   X        A           A
   I        R  U  B  B  I  S  H
   N        S           E
W  A  S  T  E              S
```

Word Search 1: Office Safety Awareness

D	I	A	T	S	R	I	F	D	Q	S	B	M	J	H
V	E	R	A	C	O	B	S	T	A	C	L	E	X	H
Z	C	D	N	B	P	I	R	T	R	N	B	R	C	B
M	I	L	A	M	C	A	Y	Z	F	A	G	E	G	R
G	F	S	U	O	I	C	S	N	O	C	E	E	R	C
V	F	M	B	N	L	J	T	A	R	I	J	U	R	M
F	O	T	I	S	N	R	N	T	F	B	L	U	Z	L
P	B	N	H	Y	G	I	E	N	E	E	J	L	Y	Y
C	G	A	M	U	L	T	D	V	S	D	T	B	P	O
H	R	R	V	A	C	R	I	K	O	A	G	Y	A	Y
P	A	D	P	X	A	Q	C	Z	R	A	U	D	C	S
Z	F	I	F	Z	F	G	C	V	L	Q	V	Q	P	T
A	Y	D	A	I	H	K	A	O	Q	U	L	D	Z	B
T	M	H	G	S	G	S	V	K	I	T	O	X	L	M

Word Search 2: Display Screen Equipment

S	Y	V	V	P	U	U	N	T	J	P	L	T	F	B
M	A	F	F	S	H	L	S	O	Y	F	S	C	B	X
U	H	K	W	T	N	E	M	P	I	U	Q	E	L	Q
F	S	B	Z	G	R	I	A	I	J	T	H	U	M	L
C	L	U	T	T	E	R	U	D	N	C	I	S	N	V
F	C	L	S	E	L	B	A	C	A	A	R	S	Q	S
D	I	I	E	U	H	M	W	K	C	C	S	I	O	S
T	R	Q	R	K	Z	R	C	A	K	J	H	N	M	P
W	K	A	T	S	Y	A	D	F	D	G	L	E	G	B
I	T	M	O	A	B	W	X	I	L	X	C	N	W	S
S	C	G	O	B	Z	S	G	A	E	I	P	W	X	C
T	F	U	F	E	Y	M	R	A	I	U	Z	E	W	L
I	J	A	H	P	N	E	H	Y	Q	A	M	A	H	C
N	Q	I	W	V	L	B	K	K	O	B	V	N	H	X
G	E	H	I	F	J	S	I	W	D	T	R	P	Q	Q

Word Search 3: Risk Assessment

M	R	A	S	E	I	R	U	J	N	I	H	R	E	S
A	E	C	N	A	N	E	T	N	I	A	M	S	J	E
N	Q	A	S	S	E	S	S	M	E	N	T	S	Y	Z
U	U	Y	M	P	Y	P	L	A	I	F	Z	E	U	E
A	I	U	Y	E	O	O	Q	N	H	C	P	N	X	Q
L	R	U	D	N	R	N	V	A	O	O	S	E	K	L
H	E	E	S	A	U	S	H	G	L	N	D	R	A	E
A	M	N	R	L	Z	I	H	E	G	D	R	A	D	C
N	E	X	W	T	Q	B	S	R	F	I	X	W	N	T
D	N	P	Y	I	C	L	O	S	I	T	C	A	E	H
L	T	R	Y	E	L	E	C	T	R	I	C	I	T	Y
I	S	D	C	S	R	O	R	R	E	O	O	S	K	M
N	S	A	M	L	G	V	D	L	T	N	I	Q	K	E
G	P	U	T	H	A	Z	A	R	D	S	C	I	D	R

Word Search 4: Safe Manual Handling

E	A	V	T	A	K	R	H	V	I	F	F	D	K	W
O	T	J	E	S	U	O	U	N	E	R	T	S	M	V
M	T	N	E	M	P	I	U	Q	E	T	H	G	M	G
H	I	H	I	S	Y	C	S	E	I	R	U	J	N	I
P	T	A	P	Q	Z	P	F	A	L	S	T	I	K	Z
O	U	G	N	I	Y	R	R	A	C	B	T	X	O	U
S	D	N	H	B	O	L	A	O	A	F	E	Q	H	N
T	E	I	M	M	V	Y	H	D	I	M	I	M	O	M
U	F	L	R	Z	U	V	B	L	S	S	L	F	U	P
R	O	I	U	H	Q	A	U	K	O	J	B	N	R	M
E	S	A	L	R	C	E	D	A	O	K	H	P	W	N
K	Z	R	Z	K	K	H	N	G	L	J	T	X	Q	U
P	H	T	W	Z	R	M	G	I	C	K	H	T	I	C
J	L	T	S	E	V	O	L	G	P	E	U	J	N	K
J	R	I	V	Y	J	C	F	M	U	S	A	U	B	L

Word Search 5: Environmental Awareness

E	R	E	H	P	S	O	M	T	A	F	H	O	E	K
N	G	C	V	O	S	W	E	J	K	P	B	R	N	N
V	C	O	E	L	C	Y	C	E	R	G	K	I	C	K
I	Z	N	M	L	I	G	B	J	B	E	K	K	S	P
R	O	O	K	U	F	R	E	T	S	A	W	S	N	D
O	I	M	C	T	R	E	N	O	Z	O	U	K	D	X
N	K	Y	H	I	V	N	M	X	Y	B	X	J	X	C
M	D	S	E	O	J	E	F	I	U	R	P	P	D	Z
E	X	H	A	N	F	E	S	N	T	M	I	T	J	C
N	J	T	P	I	B	R	D	Z	B	A	A	R	M	R
T	M	R	E	H	B	G	A	N	R	Y	N	E	R	S
A	W	A	R	E	N	E	S	S	Q	U	V	K	C	I
L	G	E	H	Y	I	D	P	W	L	R	C	M	Z	Y